The Evader

Lauren Van Gerven

Note to reader: This work depicts actual events in the life of the author's grandfather as truthfully as recollection permits and/or can be verified by research. This book is a fictional dramatization based on a true story and real events and was drawn from a variety of sources, including published materials and first person recounts. For narrative purposes, the story contains fictionalized scenes, composite and representative characters and dialogue, and time compression. The views and opinions expressed are those of the characters only and do not necessarily reflect the views and opinions held by individuals on which those characters are based. All pictures portrayed in this book are from the author's private collection.

In honor of my grandfather,
Leonard Emile Marcel Sonck

CHAPTER ONE

Belgium

"P atron, one more beer," I shouted across the empty bar.

"Same thing, Sonck?"

I nodded as the bartender took my empty glass and walked back over to the other side of the bar. He grabbed a fresh glass from the shelf above his head and tilted it at a 30-degree angle before opening the tap. The golden liquid started to flow as he slowly straightened out the glass, resulting in a perfect two-finger collar of white foam.

It was 6:30 p.m. on an early spring evening and aside from the bartender and I, there was only one other person in the pub. An old man sat silently in the corner of the room, blankly staring at the untouched beer in front of him. If his beer once had that same perfect collar as mine, it had long since evaporated.

The bartender set my pint in front of me, and I lifted it to my lips. When I placed my glass back down, I could feel the white mustache of foam left on my upper lip. I quickly wiped it off with the back of my hand. For the baby-faced 18-year-old that I was, it was the closest I could get to a real mustache.

I was born Leonard Sonck on September 25th 1922, to Maurice Sonck and Jeanne Van Laeken, a young upper-middle-class couple that called the city of Antwerp home. I was the second of a kind. In June 1921, my parents had welcomed a son by the same name as mine who had only lived to be a few weeks old. There never came any more kids after me, and thus I lived the typical slightly spoiled and somewhat overprotected life of an only child.

Life in Antwerp in the late 20s and early 30s was joyful. Although Belgium had suffered deeply during the First World War, the country recovered surprisingly fast and Antwerp even hosted the first post-war Olympic Games in 1920. I was blessed with a happy childhood. We lived in a lovely house in the center of the city, in the *Schilderstraat*, Painter Street, named so because of its location directly across from the museum of fine arts. Once the home of famous painters such as Rubens and Brueghel, as well as the world center of the diamond trade, Antwerp was a city rich in arts and culture.

As a young boy I used to accompany my mother on trips to the market, which was only a short walk from our house. My mother was a kind and classy lady, but could come across as quite intimidating. She walked around with her head high and never hesitated to call city officials if she noticed roadwork was taking longer than scheduled, or if a bus driver on a certain route was routinely a few minutes late. She was a handful, but she cared deeply about me. On our way back from the market we would always stop at one of the many chocolate shops in the city, where she would let me pick out a praline or two. Out of the almost endless selection of pralines, I always chose one of the bitter, dark chocolate ones.

My father, Maurice, worked a lot, but equally loved to entertain. It was quite common for him to come home during lunch announcing to my mother that he had invited several people over for dinner that same evening. I don't understand how she did it with only half a day's notice, but my mother always managed to produce quite the feast for my father's many guests. Although I had a happy childhood, I was a quite sickly child, which was part of the reason why, for secondary school, I was sent off to boarding school.

Around the time when I started boarding school in 1934, things had slowly started to change in Europe. In Germany, Hitler was becoming more and more powerful, while the country's violations of the Treaty of Versailles went along unpunished. I was too young at the time to truly understand what was happening in European politics, but to any adult staying up to date with the news, it was becoming clear that it was only a matter of time before the continent would once again be at war.

After several years of tension and uncertainty, in May 1940, World War II caught up to the small country I called home.

By the time I was sitting at that bar, ordering beers in that small quiet pub, it had long become clear that this would be another long run of social, political and economic uncertainty for all of Belgium and its inhabitants.

By then, in March 1941, I had been coming to pub *Het Zuid* almost every evening after work, since I had started working for my father when I returned home after I finished secondary school the previous summer.

I didn't particularly enjoy working for my father. We didn't get along that well, and what I really wanted was to return to school to study to become a lawyer. I had put my studies on hold because of the war, so working for my father would have to do for now.

Even though I sat at that bar so frequently, to an outsider walking in, I probably looked out of place.

Not only was I much younger than the average person drowning their sorrows at *Het Zuid*, I also dressed much better than anyone I had ever seen there. The pub attracted mainly working-class men in need of a beer or two after a long day of heavy labor. I, on the other hand, always dressed in a three-piece suit, my hair neatly combed back. And with the faint scent of the cologne I applied every morning still lingering, it was an understatement saying I stood out.

The only reason no one ever gave me a hard time for being there was because almost everyone on the south side of Antwerp, especially anyone working around the harbor and its inner-city docks, knew my father Maurice.

For as long as I could remember, my father had owned a ship chandlery and lumber company that specialized in flagpoles, in the Port of Antwerp.

Not only was he a successful entrepreneur, owning one of the first cars in the city, he was also a very likable person with a larger-than-life personality who was a regular at many pubs and restaurants across the city. Unlike my father, I wasn't born with the same social genes that he possessed. I was an introvert by nature.

Although he never directly told me, I always felt like it disappointed him that I, his only son, wasn't more like him.

Despite not really fitting in at *Het Zuid*, I enjoyed having my one or two beers there after work. The pub was just a block away from the lumberyard and our office, and to be quite frank, I enjoyed the people watching.

I had spent the majority of my adolescence at *Le Nid d'Aiglon*, an affluent French speaking boarding school in Heide-Kalmthout, in the northern part of the province of Antwerp. As a lifelong asthma sufferer, the country air was supposed to be good for my health. *Le Nid D'Aiglon* also didn't have any religious affiliation, which appealed to my father, who uncommonly for the time, was an atheist who didn't want his son to attend Catholic school. As a result, my secular boarding school housed predominantly Jewish kids. Sons and daughters of wealthy diamond traders and jewelers. Unlike most schools at the time, *Le Nid d'Aiglon* housed both boys and girls. The school itself might have been secular, but that wasn't to say that religion had no influence at all amongst the students. I made some great friends but was never fully accepted as one of their own by the Jewish boys. Still, I enjoyed my time at school and look back at my time in Kalmthout with great fondness.

Boarding school and *Het Zuid* felt like they belonged in two different worlds, but then again, since the beginning of the war, there were many things that felt like they belonged in a different world.

Everyday life still felt fairly normal in Antwerp in 1941, but you could feel that the Nazi influence was growing. It seemed like daily more German soldiers were arriving in the city.

Belgium had tried to stay neutral when France and England had declared war on Germany back in 1939, but it didn't last. The Belgian coastline, a gateway to a possible invasion of the United Kingdom, and the Port of Antwerp, made Belgium a much too valuable piece of real estate to leave untouched.

In May 1940, the German Army unexpectedly invaded the Low Countries. Receiving substantial support from the French, as well as over 150,000 men from the British Army, the Battle of Belgium lasted an impressive 18 days, but ended with the inevitable surrender of the Belgium Army on May 28, 1940. Nevertheless, the Belgian perseverance over those 18 days prevented the British from being cut off from the coast, enabling the evacuation from Dunkirk.

Despite putting up a great fight, the Belgian defeat forced the allied forces to withdraw from continental Europe while the Belgian government fled the country, setting up a government in exile in England, while German authorities took over.

Going against the advice of his own government, the king of Belgium, Leopold III, didn't flee the country. Disregarding a reminder from Prime Minister Hubert Pierlot that capitulation is a governmental decision, not one a king can make, Leopold argued that he wanted to stay in Belgium with his troops.

While the ministers thought Leopold might establish a new government under Hitler, a treasonous act, the king argued that the country would see him as a deserter if he were to leave his country.

What his true intentions were, can only be speculated upon.

Eventually Leopold became a prisoner of the Third Reich, but was allowed to stay at his home, sitting out the rest of the war at his palace in Laeken near Brussels. Not the worst way to sit out the remainder of the war.

I have never been very political by nature, but I wasn't a big supporter of the idea of Belgium trying to stay neutral. In the far western corner of our country, the World War I graves of thousands of British soldiers had barely been covered long enough to be overgrown with grass. Yet here we were, merely 20 years later, declaring that we didn't want to join Great Britain and France in their fight against Germany. It felt cowardly, and when taking geography into consideration, it seemed unrealistic thinking that the Germans would let us sit this one out. But, at the same time, as a young adolescent, I wasn't exactly jumping up and down to serve in the Belgian Army. I knew very well that we were being slaughtered and that at my young age, with no experience, they would put me in the most dangerous situations, which is why in 1940, when Belgian was fighting a battle it would inevitably lose, I ignored the government's call for all age-eligible man to report for duty. I stayed in Antwerp and decided to wait for a time when I knew I could make an impact.

By 1941 the Germans had made great headway in their pursuit of conquering Europe. It felt like all the news we received, even that outside of the propaganda distributed by the Germans, brought nothing but updates of German victories. The chances of an allied win looked to be diminishing day by day.

That cold evening in March 1941, an evening that started out like any other evening at *Het Zuid*, unexpectedly ended up being the beginning of my World War II story.

Just as I was finishing my beer the door opened and two German soldiers in full uniform, with their visor caps and perfectly polished boots, entered the pub.

Neither of them could have looked any more German. Hitler himself would have very much approved of them, with their blond hair, blue eyes, athletic built and strong jaw lines. If one wasn't half a head taller than the other one, they could have easily been mistaken for twins.

It wasn't uncommon at the time to see German soldiers around town eating and drinking at local restaurants and pubs. They usually caused no harm, but you could always feel a change in atmosphere the second a German entered an establishment. Everybody instantly became a touch more tense.

As soon as the soldiers walked through the pub's door, it was evident that this wasn't the first pub they had visited that evening. They were being loud, laughing amongst themselves, and you could tell that they had been drinking by the way they moved. The shorter one of the pair could barely walk straight.

"Two beers!" one of the soldiers shouted when he was halfway from the entrance to the counter.

They sat down next to me at the bar and downed their beers within minutes, while talking much louder than necessary for an almost empty bar.

I quietly listened as they pestered the bartender with questions on why there weren't any girls at the bar.

The bartender shrugged, trying to avoid their questions, but they wouldn't let it go.

Their behavior made my skin crawl, but I told myself not to interfere.

Bored of the bartender's lack of reaction, one of the soldiers redirected his attention to me.

"Funeral?"

The taller soldier had turned towards me and addressed me with this single word.

"Excuse me?" I countered, slightly annoyed.

"The suit," he said. "I can only think of two reasons why one would wear a suit like that, and you don't look like you just came from a wedding."

"Just work," I replied, keeping my answer as short as possible.

I was happy that he left our conversation at that and didn't try to ask me any more questions. Small talk with Germans wasn't exactly one of my preferred activities.

He turned back to the bartender and the two soldiers started talking amongst themselves.

Although my German language skills aren't great, I understand enough to know that they were talking behind the bartender's back. I could hear them making fun of the old man's large ears.

Out of nowhere, I suddenly felt an inexplicable rage coming over me. I could feel a never before experienced level of anger towards the war, and these German soldiers in particular, building up inside of me.

I took a deep breath, followed by another sip of my beer, in an attempt to calm myself.

Next to me, the soldiers tried to order two more beers, but the bartender told them he was about to close.

This was news that didn't exactly go over well.

"It's not even 7 p.m., what kind of pub closes this early? I thought you Belgians at least knew something about drinking beer, but apparently even that's too much to ask in this silly little country," the soldier sitting closest to me shouted.

The shouting, in addition to the alcohol, had turned his face bright red.

Everything about their attitude and behavior annoyed me. I'm not quite sure what motivated me to do what happened next, or where I was even planning to go with it, but for some reason, before I could stop myself, I spoke up.

"Gentlemen," I said. "I know of another pub that stays open until the darkest hours of the night and has the most beautiful girls in all of Antwerp. If you'd like, I can show you where it is."

The soldiers, although slightly surprised by my sudden interference, didn't hesitate long.

"Finally, a Belgian who appreciates the better things in life. Show us where this place is, and it better not disappoint."

The bartender shot me a confused look.

I put five francs down on the bar to settle my tab, stood up, put on my coat and told the soldiers to follow me.

I had no clue of where to find a pub with beautiful women serving beers all night long, and even if I did, I wouldn't have brought these men there.

Although at this point the city wasn't under curfew unless a killing of German personnel had taken place, most pubs and restaurants still closed early out of general precaution. Once the sun set, it became very dark around the city as street lights stayed turned off and residents covered their windows so that the city wouldn't be as easy to spot for warplanes flying over.

I walked the soldiers out of the pub, into the frigid evening air. We were the only people out on the cobblestoned street. The pub was located right on the edge of the inner-city Port of Antwerp docks, but it was so dark that you couldn't even see the water 40 feet in front of us. Until the moment I walked out of the pub, I had no plan whatsoever, but suddenly I knew what I was going to do.

"Where is this great pub you speak of," the soldier to my left asked. He was so drunk that he was slurring his words.

"It's really close by, as a matter of fact, it's right across the marketplace. Do you see the little lights on the other side of the square?" I asked as I positioned myself in between both soldiers and pointed in the distance, across the docks, which in the dark could have easily been mistaken for a large market square.

"Let's go!" the drunkest one of the two yelled out.

Walking between the two soldiers, I guided them confidently towards the water.

After about twenty paces, I bent over, pretending to tie my shoelace, as the two men continued on. I got back up just in time to see the shorter soldier disappear over the edge, dropping down into the dock.

The second soldier had managed to stop just short of the water. He was wildly floundering, his arms in the air, trying to keep his balance in an attempt to avoid the same faith as his comrade.

I quickly ran up to him and gave him a big push in the back.

He went flying over the edge, dropping 20ft down into the dock's icy cold water.

In broad daylight, if the fall hadn't knocked them out, it would have been fairly easy for them to find one of the steel ladders attached to the side of the dock. But now, in the dark and intoxicated as they were, they would have to get lucky to find the ladder before drowning.

I heard the man scream as he hit the water, but didn't wait around to see what happened next.

That's two less Nazi's we need to worry about, I thought to as I walked away.

I went home and had dinner with my parents like any other evening. With my dad seated at the head of the table, my mom to his right and me to left, the three of us sat our long solid wooden dining room table, shared a meal and discussed the events of the past day. My parents did most of the talking, but that wasn't unusual. Somehow I managed to get through dinner alright, but that night I lay in bed, unable to sleep, thinking about my future.

Unless one of the soldiers had survived, the chances of me getting caught were small. Even so, it would be risky to stay. I felt fairly certain that nobody had seen me, but I couldn't know for sure.

I had been toying around with the idea of leaving Belgium for a while now, and now I had the perfect excuse to go ahead and do it.

The war would not end anytime soon, and I knew that we young men wouldn't be left alone much longer. As an inexperienced 18-year-old with severe asthma, I needed to be smart about how I wanted things to evolve.

There were rumors going around town that soon they would start sending young men to labor camps in Germany to work in factories making supplies for the war. I would have rather been shot than helped the Nazis with their war efforts.

There was no longer a Belgian Army, and even if there were, I wasn't about to get myself killed after most likely getting positioned as cannon fodder. I had been lucky that I hadn't been caught for failing to report for duty when in 1940 I had ignored the call to go fight. Regardless, it was time for me to make a move. I knew that there were quite a few Belgians, especially those who had lived closer to the frontlines of the 18-day war, who had fled the country back in 1940, making their way to England through France, some even going as far as Portugal to find a way to Great Britain, but I knew little about how they had made it there, all I knew was that it had become increasingly difficult to evade as time went on. Borders had closed to refugees by now, and very few were still taking on the journey.

Escape routes and affiliation with the resistance definitely weren't topics that were openly discussed. But at the beginning of the war, when I was fishing up school at *Le Nid d'Aiglon*, there had been a lot of rumors that several of our teachers were active members of the resistance, and that our principal, Eugène Cougnet, was the leader of the group. Mr. Cougnet was in his late forties when I attended *Le Nid d'Aiglon* but with his long grey beard and round spectacles he looked at least ten years older. He was strict, but had a gentle side to him, and was known to be very French minded. It was even said that he was a bit of an anti-Fleming.

The thought that one could be a teacher by day and a member of the resistance by night was fascinating to me, but I left school before ever being able to find out more about what exactly was going on at my boarding school.

Maybe it was time to pay a visit to my old stomping grounds to see if I could find out more about the resistance and possible escape routes.

The following morning I came up with an excuse for my father for why I had to go to my old school instead of to work and headed out to Kalmthout.

All schools had shut down during the invasion, but once the fighting had stopped, everything had returned more or less back to normal.

It was the first time I returned to my alma mater since I graduated.

The school was located in a beautiful old manor house on a large domain that included a pond in which the students would often swim on warm days. The curriculum at *Le Nid d'Aiglon* had a larger than normal focus on physical exercise and extra-curricular activities, which included unusual classes such as introductory courses to diamond cutting. Although the lectures were demanding, and education remained the number one priority, the school, with its elaborate gardens and pond, almost looked like a fancy summer camp instead of an educational institution.

Entering the school grounds, everything looked exactly the same as when I was a student there, but it felt strange to be back.

I walked into the front office and asked the secretary, who was still the same lady, if I could speak to Mr. Cougnet. To my surprise, she told me he was no longer at the school. Just a month earlier the principal had moved a part of the school to a castle somewhere in the Ardennes in the southern part of Belgium, to a secret location where it would be a safer environment for the Jewish students. The fact that he was hiding a group of students in a remote part of the country pretty much confirmed that he was part of the resistance, but it didn't help me. I couldn't exactly ask the secretary if there were any other teachers available to talk with me about the resistance and their sabotage activities, so I thanked her and left the office.

I felt disappointed that I had driven all the way out to Kalmthout just to find that Cougnet was no longer there, but I wasn't sure what else I could do.

I stepped out into the courtyard and lit my pipe. I was in deep thought, trying to figure out what to do next, when my former history teacher suddenly tapped me on the shoulder.

"I thought that was you, Leo!" he exclaimed cheerfully. "What brings you back to this neck of the woods?"

Mr. Pierot was a favorite teacher to many. He was one of the younger professors at the school and was always in a good mood. He had a friendly face, was intelligent and kind, and was the type of guy that every mother hopes her daughter ends up marrying. He seemed like too nice of a person to ever wish any harm upon another, even if that other was an enemy of the state, so I couldn't imagine him being a potential member of the resistance, but I trusted him enough to tell him the true reason why I was there.

"I'm thinking about leaving the country, heading to England," I told him, getting straight to the point. "I heard that there might be people here who can point me in the right direction, give me some pointers on how to get started."

I put my pipe back in the side of my mouth and looked right at my former teacher, whose face had suddenly turned more serious than I had ever seen it before.

"Let's continue this conversation in my office."

I followed the history teacher in silence, neither of us saying a single word as we walked through the school halls. I wasn't used to seeing Pierot this quiet and serious, but once in his office, with the door safely closed behind us, he relaxed and the smile I was so used to seeing slowly returned to his face.

He plunged down in the maroon leather chair behind his antique desk, gestured for me to take a seat across from him, and folded his arms behind his head.

After a long pause, he finally broke the silence.

"So you think you want to leave, huh, Leo?" he asked, continuing before I had a chance to reply. "Either you're stupid, you did something stupid or, heck, maybe you know something we don't know. Whatever the reason is, know that it won't be a straightforward journey. It's not 1940 anymore, son. Borders are closed, the Germans are making fast progress."

He paused again and looked at me. Really looked at me, as if he was trying to look inside of my mind to see how serious I really was about this.

"But," he took a deep breath before continuing. "I will tell you everything I know to help you on the right path."

I couldn't help but smile. I knew my favorite teacher wouldn't leave me hanging.

As it turned out, Pierot played a much larger role in the resistance than I ever could have guessed. Even though he wasn't directly taking part in any sabotage activities, he had been one of the first members of the Belgian resistance when along with several other teachers at *Le Nid d'Aiglon* he had helped a shot down English RAF pilot escape the country not long after the Belgium Campaign had ended. Since those early days in the summer of 1940 he had made many contacts in the small world that was the Belgian resistance. He was involved with the Belgian

Legion, which later became L'*Armée Secrète*, the Secret Army, and the *Joods Verdedigingscomiteit*, a group that focused on helping Jewish children find a safe refuge.

He told me that if I was serious about wanting to leave Belgium, I needed to visit Colonel Robert Lentz, the chief of the Belgian Legion, as he would be one of very few people who wouldn't laugh straight at my face if I told him I wanted to leave the country. He scribbled down Lentz's address at *37 l'Avenue Huart Hamoir* in Brussels and wished me the best of luck.

On Saturday I took the train to Brussels to pay a visit to Colonel Lentz. It had been four days since that fateful evening at *Het Zuid*. Every passing day, first thing in the morning, I checked the local newspaper to see if there was a story about the two soldiers. I kept expecting to see a large front-page photo of two dead German soldiers with the docks in the background, but it never came.

They had put the city on curfew, which was fair to assume was a direct consequence of my actions, but one of the high-up German officers must have blocked the newspapers from reporting on the incident. I had avoided *Het Zuid* on Wednesday, but had returned on Thursday so I wouldn't be suspiciously absent.

I didn't hear a word about the incident at the pub, but on Friday I had overheard a few of the workers at the lumberyard talking about two bodies that had been recovered from the docks.

"It was probably an accident," one of the men had suggested.

"Don't be stupid, Jef," the other countered. "Accidents don't happen to two men at the same time. There's got to be more to it."

In the end, they agreed that there was no telling what might have happened, but that either way the soldiers had probably deserved what had happened to them. All I could hope for was that the authorities had the same way of thinking about it.

My trip to Brussels went smoothly. I boarded a train in Antwerp's central station, which took me straight to the capital. From there, I hopped over to another train that went to Schaerbeek, one of Brussels suburbs.

German officers were present on almost all of the trains during the war, but unless the train was crossing into a different country, or something looked suspicious, the officers rarely bothered the passengers.

Avenue Huart Hamoir was located just a two-minute walk from the Schaerbeek train station, which made it easy for me to find Colonel Lentz's house.

The avenue was lined with similar style houses with in between them a large central lawn that ended in a park. It seemed like a nice place to live.

The colonel's house was a beautiful narrow three-story baroque house with a blue front door.

The entire train ride I had been thinking about what to say once I would ring Colonel Lentz's doorbell, but by the time I was standing in front of his door, I still hadn't quite figured out how to approach the situation. "Good morning, my name is Leo, I hear you're the head of the Belgian resistance," probably wouldn't work out too well.

I had been standing in front of the house for a good five minutes, making myself nervous, when the door suddenly opened.

It was the Colonel himself.

"Are you just going to stand in front of my door kid, or are you actually going to come in?" he said, sounding frustrated as he shook his head.

I must not have looked like a serious threat for him to just come forward and invite me into his house.

"You're not the first 18-year-old to show up on my doorstep," he explained as soon as he closed the door behind me. "I can't have guys like you hanging around in front of my house, it doesn't look good. I'd rather just risk it and at least pull you into my hallway."

He was speaking to me as if I was an old friend's son whom he had known for years. He didn't act suspicious of me at all and sounded almost like he had been expecting me. His tone completely threw me off, especially since he didn't look even half as kind as he sounded.

Colonel Lentz was an earnest-looking man in his mid-fifties who had been born into a military family. His father Charles was an officer who had served in the second regiment of Ligne in the late 1800s. Lentz himself entered the School of

Cadets on his 16th birthday and went on to play an important role in the First World War, especially during the battle for Healen in August 1914. More recently, during the 18-day Battle for Belgium in May 1940, he served as Chief of Staff for the 17th Infantry Division. When the fighting concluded he was famously quoted saying, "This is just a tactical mishap, the war continues."

Along with several other key figures, he immediately started regrouping and by the end of 1940 *l'Armée Belge* had been restored.

"Well son, are you at least going to tell me who told you to come here?" he asked as we both still stood in his hallway. "I won't let you up the stairs unless you give me that information."

Regaining my ability to speak after the strangeness of the past minute, I told the colonel I had been a student at *Le Nid d'Aiglon* and that it was my former teacher who had told me where to find him.

"Fair enough. Follow me to my living room."

The colonel turned around and started walking up the stairs. I hesitantly followed him up the narrow stairway.

His upstairs living room was elegantly decorated with dark wooden furniture and various shades of maroon but there were stacks of documents piled up everywhere I looked.

If the Gestapo were to drop by, it wouldn't take them long to gather enough evidence to sentence the Colonel to death, I thought.

He walked over to his armchair, sat down and without inviting me to take a seat started to talk.

He didn't ask a single question about why I had come to see him, or how exactly I thought I could contribute to the war effort. Instead, he jumped right into how I could possibly make it to liberated territory and from there on to England without being caught.

"To make it to England, you'll have to cross five borders," he started. "Some will be tougher to cross than others, but don't think that a single part of the journey will be easy."

At the time, France was divided into three major zones. The northern part of France, which ran along the Flemish border, was under the authority of the Military

Administration of Belgium and Northern France and was known as *la zone rouge*; the red zone. In that part of the country, one couldn't move around freely without official documents signed by German authorities. Moving south, the next zone was Occupied France, a territory that included the area bordering the Atlantic Ocean and ran to about 200km south of Paris. If you made it through these two zones you reached the *Zone Libre*, the southern part of France which was ruled by the government in Vichy, an area in which one can move around freely.

"But don't be mistaken," the Colonel warned me. "They often see Belgians as the enemy all around France, and many French people wouldn't so much as give a glass of water to Belgian refugees."

"Don't think that you've made it past the worst when you make it to the Free Zone," Lentz continued. "Things might calm down for a bit, but crossing the Pyrenees to get into Spain might be one of the physically and mentally toughest things you'll ever have to do. And you'll be lucky not to get arrested once you make it to the other side. Those Spaniards are a bunch of fascists."

Apparently the thought of Spain angered him. He suddenly got up, walked over to his liquor cabinet and poured himself a drink. Without offering me anything, he returned and continued.

Getting to the planning side of things, Lentz told me that he could get me false papers that could get me safely through the Red Zone. The paperwork itself was fairly easily falsifiable. He would draft some documents that looked just like the ones the German authorities issued. These documents would give me the authority to travel to Paris to visit a so-called sick relative. The toughest part would be keeping my cool and sticking to my made-up story when a German officer would inevitably check my documents during the train journey. The colonel advised me to come up with as many details as possible about why I had to go to Paris. Things like who I would be visiting, where I would be staying, and what was wrong with my relative, but he warned me not to memorize a set sequence of phrases, so that the conversation would flow as natural as possible when speaking to the officer.

The drink seemed to have taken the edge off Lentz and he was now all business, providing me with all the information I needed to successfully take on the journey.

He gave me the names and addresses of several resistance members and safe houses along the way and insisted I memorize all the details, as writing down any information could put someone's life in danger in case I got arrested.

I left Avenue Huart Hamoir feeling both encouraged that someone believed I could successfully complete this journey, and didn't think that I was crazy for considering it, motivated to get going, but also a little anxious and even a bit worried about the travels that lay ahead of me. But there was no time for fear. I quickly dismissed any feelings of doubt. I knew that if I wanted to make it to England; I needed to stop hesitating and get going. It was now or never.

Back in Antwerp, I tried to act like nothing had changed. The entire next week I went to work just like I did at any other time and continued my almost nightly visits to pub *Het Zuid*. Talking to other customers at the pub, the case of the drowned German soldiers came up once or twice, and when it did, I reacted with mediocre interest and tried to quickly move on to the next subject. The fact that there was still being talked about the incident gave me a feel of urgency to leave. I couldn't be taking any unnecessary risks.

At home, I didn't tell my parents anything about my plans to leave the country.

Of course I worried about how concerned they would be to find me gone, and about how they would worry about me, but I knew that they wouldn't agree with my decision and I couldn't risk having them trying to talk me out of it. The less they knew about where I was going, the better it would be for all of us.

Lentz had told me it would take a couple of days for him to prepare my paperwork in order to enter the Red Zone. We had settled on the following Sunday for me to meet back up with the Colonel and collect my needed paperwork.

I had no clue of what I was getting myself into, which also meant that I didn't need much time or many supplies to get ready for my journey. I did make a quick trip to the bank where I emptied my entire savings account, the value of about three months worth of salaries. I thought about leaving a little for my return, but things were so uncertain that I figured I might as well take all of it.

During the days between my visit to Brussels and my departure, I came up with a story about a made-up sick relative. I made sure to memorize the list of contacts and addresses Lentz had given me, and I gathered a few belongings that I decided I would take with me. I didn't want to bring too much as I figured it would look suspicious, so I packed just enough clothes to where it looked like I would spend a few days with my relatives.

I decided to leave straight after my meeting with Colonel Lentz.

My parents were early risers regardless of the day of the week, but I figured leaving on Sunday might buy me a bit of extra time before my parents noticed I had gone missing. The three of us typically had an extensive breakfast on Sunday morning and I couldn't help but feel a wave of guilt at the thought of my parents sitting at our dining room table, all by themselves, not knowing where their only son had gone.

Saturday evening was tough. Although I never second-guessed my plan to leave the country, sitting at dinner with my parents I wondered when, or even if, we would all three sit at this table to share a meal again.

I looked at my parents' faces in a way I had never looked at them before, a much deeper way, as if I was trying to memorize every single detail of their faces exactly as they were in that moment.

I rarely spoke much during dinner, my dad was the big story teller, not me, but I must have been especially quiet as my mother asked me twice if I was doing okay, and if the meal tasted good. I assured her that everything was just fine and that the food tasted delicious, but I'm sure she sensed that something was off. There's no fooling a mother's intuition.

Not much later, I kissed both my parents goodnight and retreated to my room. Needless to say, I didn't get much sleep that night. As I lay in my childhood room, I wondered where I would be sleeping the following night. I wondered about the places I would see and the people I would meet along the way.

Thinking about my parents that evening, I decided I didn't want to leave without at least leaving a note. I grabbed a piece of paper and scribbled down a brief message, that I later left on the kitchen counter.

Simple and direct, it read:

Dear mother and father,

I can no longer sit back and watch as the Germans take over our streets. I have decided to leave Belgium in search of a place where I can make myself of use. Please do not worry about me. Until we meet again.

Your loving son,
Leonard.

Early in the morning, on Sunday, March 23rd 1941, I snuck out of my parental home, not knowing when I would return. Doing my best not to wake up my father who was a notoriously light sleeper, I tiptoed down the stairs and quietly closed the front door behind me. It was just before sunrise and most of the city was sound asleep. Still standing on the doorstep, I took a moment to take in the city's peacefulness, then I turned around, took one last look at the house I grew up in before turning my back and officially starting my journey south.

CHAPTER TWO

The Journey

From my parents' house, I walked the kilometer or so to Antwerp's grand central station. The station, which was completed in the early 1900s, with its impressively high ceilings designed so to deal with the smoke of steam locomotives, was one of Antwerp's most beautiful and recognizable buildings. With its large overarching dome built out of iron and glass, it almost looked like a giant, yet elegant birdcage that had been dropped in the middle of the city.

I entered through the main doors that gave way to the foyer. The floor of the vast entry hall was covered with large gray and white square tiles that made the foyer look like an enormous chessboard. I made my way across the hall towards a massive three-pronged stairway with behind it high arches cut out of heavy stone and at the top, a clock, there to keep the station's many travelers aware of the time.

I ran up the stairway leading to the platforms. There was barely anybody at the station so early in the morning, and with every step I climbed, the sound of my shoes tapping on the stone floor echoed around the empty hall.

By the time the sun rose and the city slowly started to wake, I was standing on one of the platforms that I had stood on countless times before, yet this time felt unlike any other. I nervously smiled and nodded at the few other people who were also waiting for the first train to Brussels. They gave me blank stares in response. There had been little to smile about since the beginning of the war, and most people were becoming increasingly suspicious of strangers.

My plan for my first day on the road was simple. First, I would travel to Brussels where I was to meet with Colonel Lentz who would supply me with the documents necessary to make it through the Red Zone or *Zone Interdite*, the forbidden zone. Once I was in possession of those documents, along with my made up excuse for traveling, I should be clear to travel to Paris without any real issues.

To make it to Paris, I would have to cross the Closed Zone, an area stretching across the southern border of Belgium and along the eastern side of France down to the border of the Free Zone. Once I had passed through the Closed Zone, there was no turning back, as return was prohibited for refugees and anyone trying to return to the Military Administration of Belgium and Northern France.

From Brussels I would travel on to Abbeville, a city about 50 kilometers south of Lille, the first city across the Belgian border. From there I would take another train on to the French capital. Paris would mark the end of the initial leg of my journey.

Other than some early morning merchants and a few other travelers, the train to the Belgian capital was empty. We picked up a few more passengers at some stops along the way, but by the time we reached Brussels more than an hour later, the train was still only half full.

It was 8:42 a.m. when the train pulled into the station. I had agreed to meet Colonel Lentz at the café just inside the entrance of the train station at 9 o'clock. The timing gave me more than enough time to familiarize myself with the documents before boarding my train to France, which was scheduled to leave just before ten. I walked over to the café and was happy to find the Colonel already sitting at a corner table with a cup of coffee in front of him, turning through the morning paper.

I doubt it was an enjoyable read as any Belgian paper that was still in circulation was now run by the Germans and the so-called news was edited accordingly.

He startled as I sat down in the chair across from him.

"Sonck," he said, with a hint of surprise in his voice, as if he hadn't expected me to show.

He took off his glasses, neatly folded the newspaper in four, put it down on the table and picked up the briefcase that had been sitting on the floor next to our table.

Our entire interaction so far had existed of that one word he had uttered when he had first noticed my presence.

Apart from the server who looked only half awake when I glanced over to order myself a weak cup of coffee, we were the only people in the café.

From his briefcase, Lentz handed me the latest copy of *Signal*, a German propaganda magazine.

Oh, the irony, I thought as I opened the magazine to find my documents hidden inside the centerfold.

The two of us sat there for an appropriate amount of time, drinking our coffees and quietly discussing my documents and what to do if I were to be questioned about them. I was now in possession of the needed documentation to, more or less legally, enter France.

Entering France was expected to be one of the easier parts of my journey. Crossing the border into Spain would be a lot more challenging, as it was highly unlikely that I would be able to secure forged documents that would allow me to legally cross the border. But those were worries for later. First, I needed to get to Paris.

Soon enough, it was time for me to go. I stood up, shook the Colonel's hand and walked away. Halfway to the door, I heard Lentz speak up.

"Sonck," he said again.

I turned around to face him.

"Enjoy your trip!" He shouted out, a big smile on his face.

I gave him a quick nod, then walked out to go catch my train.

I made it to Paris without much excitement along the way. As expected, two German officers had come around to check all passengers' paperwork as we approached the French border. In the spring of 1941 it was not yet out of the ordinary for someone to travel across the Belgian-French border to visit relatives. When asked upon inspection of my papers, I told the officers that I was traveling to Paris to visit my elderly grandmother.

I made sure to speak with confidence, while showing the needed amount of respect. Neither officer seemed very interested in me, and they moved along to the next passenger without any further questions.

Off to a good start, I thought. Maybe this wasn't going to be as tough as I had expected it to be.

Apart from my quick trips to Brussels and my old boarding school, I hadn't left Antwerp much since the start of the war. As such, my train ride through the northern French countryside felt like an eye-opening experience.

The war was definitely present everywhere you looked in Antwerp, but the city had not yet been the target of any bombings, so its buildings and infrastructure looked as it always had.

The Nord-Pas-de-Calais hadn't been so lucky. When the train started to slow in preparation for our arrival in Abbeville, the destruction was clearly noticeable from my window. Abbeville had been hit hard during the Battle of France the previous year. Everywhere I looked there seemed to be bomb damage, even their cathedral hadn't been spared.

I switched trains in Abbeville. There were few people waiting at the station and those who I did see looked like shells of their former selves. Everyone looked tired and worn as they stared silently into the distance.

I stood on the platform, lost in my thoughts, as a steady mist of tiny raindrops descended on the city. It was cold and gloomy out, adding to the already depressing surroundings. I wasn't far from home at all, yet things seemed very different here. In Antwerp, we hadn't seen the same 1940 as people here had. I hadn't seen a single explosion firsthand since the war had started. Here, bombs had landed in people's kitchens and dining rooms, here, people had lost their houses and some even family members. Those were deeply sobering thoughts. I was glad I didn't have to wait long for my next train to arrive. I didn't know what to expect ahead, in Paris and further south, but I felt a sense of relief when I boarded the train taking me away from Abbeville and its dreariness.

I arrived in Paris by nightfall. Thanks to Colonel Lentz I had addresses to safe houses both in Paris and in Bordeaux where I would be heading next.

Lentz's contact in Paris was a Calvinist pastor living just a few blocks from the Gare d'Austerlitz train station. Earlier during the month there had been quite an uproar in the city, and particularly its religious circles, when another Calvinist pastor, Marc Boegner, had publicly condemned the Vichy *Statut des Juifs*. It was one of the first French public condemnation of antisemitism since the start of the war. Despite the, mostly unwanted, extra attention this had brought to the entire Parisian Calvinist church, Lentz felt no concern sending me to this particular contact.

After a short walk from the station, I arrived at Pasteur Bernard's residence in the 13th arrondissement. Bernard was a young pastor in his mid-twenties whose beliefs were very much in line with those of Pasteur Boegner. He condemned the anti-Jewish laws that had gone into effect, and gladly came to the assistance of any political refugees as well. When he spoke to me on these topics, he spoke with so much passion that you could tell he had to keep himself from raising his voice. He reminded me more of a young politician than a young pastor.

After we had dinner, a simple meal of vegetable soup with chunks of potatoes, accompanied with a, becoming increasingly rare, glass of red wine, we headed to Pasteur Bernard's church where I would be spending the night.

The church was fairly small and very soberly decorated. Unlike most Catholic Churches I had seen in Belgium, the walls here were painted white and there was very little art displayed.

A small bed had been set up for me in the sacristy, at the back of the church where the pastor's vestments were kept. Pasteur Bernard handed me some blankets, warning that the night could get very cold in the unheated building, and told me that he would be back first thing in the morning to bid me farewell.

The night was indeed very cold, but the bed was comfortable and despite the chilly temperatures I fell right asleep. The excitement and nerves of my first day of travel had worn me out.

Pasteur Bernard returned just before sunrise. He brought me some coffee and a small baguette stuffed with French cheese. An absolute luxury for the times we were living in.

"Don't eat it all at once, save a piece for your train journey," he advised me.

I thanked him for his hospitality and started gathering my affairs in order to leave for the train station.

My train for Bordeaux would be leaving in just over an hour. I was about to head out when the pastor asked me to join him in prayer. He wanted to pray for a safe continuation of my journey and for all those impacted by this horrible war.

His religious side is coming out after all, I thought.

I had no idea how to pray, and no genuine desire to do so either, but I couldn't turn him down after the hospitality he had shown me, so I reluctantly agreed to pray with him.

We kneeled down next to each other on the front row of the empty church, facing a statue of Jesus Christ on the cross. The pastor closed his eyes and started praying out loud.

Completely out of my comfort zone, I felt uneasy and couldn't get myself to close my eyes, but as I quietly listened to the words he said, a feeling of calmness slowly came over me.

His prayer sounded like the recital of a beautiful poem. He prayed for those who were upset and confused, that they would gain perspective and understanding. He prayed for those who were hurt to heal and for those who had experienced losses to find new wealths, whether material or spiritual. Finally, he prayed for a safe and successful continuation of my journey and for my journey to be purposeful.

I left Paris with a good feeling. Pasteur Bernard had been one of the first people I had met in a long time who truly believed that the Allies had a chance at winning this war. His optimism was contagious. Things weren't looking good in the spring of 1941 and few people dared to even dream of an Allied victory and even fewer dared to speak this dream out loud. But meeting people like Pasteur Bernard and hearing stories like that of Pasteur Boegner gave me hope. There were people all across occupied Europe willing to stick out their neck for what they believed in and what they thought was right.

My train to Bordeaux left Paris Gare d'Austerlitz at 9:15 a.m. The journey would take all day as I were to travel over 500 kilometers south. I felt as relaxed as one could feel for war-time travel about this leg of the journey. I wouldn't be crossing any specific borders as the entire route from Paris to Bordeaux traveled through Occupied France.

As the train made its way through the French capital, I caught a glimpse of the Eiffel Tower.

Since the invasion, the city's most famous landmark had been accessorized by the Germans. Just above the middle part of the tower hung a large banner with the slogan *"Deutschland Siegt auf allen Fronten,"* letting the citizens of Paris know that Germany is vicious on all fronts. Above the banner was a large letter V displayed. The Allies' V-for-Victory had become so popular as a morale raiser that the Germans had no choice but to adopt it. I rolled my eyes at the fact that, embarrassingly enough, their V for victory should have been an S for *Sieg*.

As the train left the city and the urban scenery made way for a more rural one, I settled into my second-class cabin and spent the majority of the day looking at the landscape rolling by outside the window.

Around noon I ate the remainder of my baguette, feeling thankful that Pasteur Bernard had held me from eating it in its entirety for breakfast. The day passed slowly and uneventfully, which I realized very well wasn't such a bad thing.

As the train approached Bordeaux, fields and orchards filled with fruit trees slowly made way for vineyards.

It maddened me to think that the Germans were now taking possession of all the great French wines.

Taking their wine away from the French should be enough to convince more than a few to join the resistance, I thought, as the train started losing speed and slowly pulled into the Bordeaux-Saint-Jean station not long after dusk.

I found my way to the second safe house of my trip and was once again welcomed warmly. This time, I stayed with a young married couple. A local baker who was part of the Bordeaux resistance network, and his lovely wife.

As the wife, Marie, served me a plate of hot dinner, the baker, Jean-Francois, went on and on about the challenges of owning a bakery without the availability of butter.

"Not a single one of the ingredients to make our precious *Canelés De Bordeaux* is readily available," he told me, his voice filled with frustration. "No butter, there are barely any eggs, let alone any rum!"

His passion for his work was evident. He longed for the day when his shop window would once again be overflowing with croissants and eclairs and mille-feuilles. Simply hearing him describe his pastries made my mouth water.

That night, I went to bed feeling sad for France. A France without wine or pastries is simply not a France worth living in.

Despite Jean-Francois' lack of supplies, I was still awakened by the smells of freshly baked bread drifting up the stairs from the bakery located below. I was hungry and badly wanted to head downstairs and bite my teeth into a warm and crunchy piece of freshly baked baguette, but I had been told to stay hidden in the small guest room until someone came to get me. It was still dark out and when I picked up my watch, the hands read quarter to five. I decided to turn around and quickly fell into a sleep filled with dreams of pastries and baguettes.

My dream more or less became reality when at 7:30 a.m. Marie came to my room with a piece of bread and apricot jam. She told me that I would have to stay in hiding for the remainder of the day as they didn't want anybody to notice their unknown guest. After sunset, I would accompany Jean-Francois to a fellow resistance member's house who would be able to help me with the next step of my journey.

The first two legs of my journey had been relatively easy, but after Bordeaux things would get a little more challenging.

It was easier to cross into Spain from the eastern side of France, which meant that I would first have to traverse the demarcation line into the *Zone Libre*. The more hilly parts of the Pyrenees, some of which could be reached from occupied France, were less heavily patrolled, but with my asthma I was worried that I wouldn't be able to handle the climb.

I spent the day passing the time by reading a book that Marie had given me and waiting for the bakery to close. When Jean-Francois finally finished his long work day, we had a quick meal and as soon as the sun had set we ventured out to meet his friend, Emile.

Emile was a winemaker who owned a small vineyard just outside of the city. In protest of being forced to sell his entire harvest, severely below market price, to the Germans for the past two years, he had joined the local resistance. What he really wanted to do was add rat poison to his currently fermenting wine, but since that would have been a little too obvious, he stuck to minor acts of rebellion like smuggling people across the demarcation line.

The vintner shook my hand and welcomed me into his home. Despite his calloused hands, undoubtedly from years of hard work around the property, and his strong build, he had a warm smile. At first impression, he looked like the kind of guy you wouldn't want to have as an enemy, but a great friend if you're lucky enough to have him on your side.

We spent the next few hours discussing a plan for crossing into the Free Zone and the potential challenges we might face.

The demarcation line, almost 1200 kilometers long in its entirety, was too large of an area for the Germans to keep guarded at all places, but occupying authorities kept a close watch on it at all times and security and patrols had been on the rise. There were only four official crossing points for the demarcation line and only one in the southern part of France, in Langon, which was more than fifty kilometers southeast of Bordeaux.

The only way for a foreigner to legally cross the line was if one could present an *Ausweis*, a pass that was only issued by the German authorities, the *Kommandanturen*, and had to be presented in addition to one's identity card. Since it would have been practically impossible for me to obtain such a pass, we were limited to the illegal ways of crossing into Vichy France. Hiding me in a car or buggy while someone in possession of a pass crossed the line at the official checkpoint had become increasingly difficult after several smugglers had been caught. The option that was most likely to succeed was to sneak across the demarcation line at an unguarded point.

Emile knew a fellow winemaker in Langon whose vineyards bordered the demarcation line. The farmer had assisted him in a previous smuggle, and Emile felt sure that he would be willing to help again.

If the farmer agreed, the plan would be as follows: I would travel to Langon with Emile, where we would stay at his friend's vineyard. Residents who lived within 10 kilometers of the line were allowed to apply for an *Ausweis für den kleinen Grenzverkehr*, a specific pass for local cross-border travel. Since the farmer was in possession of such a pass, he would legally cross the checkpoint while at the same time I crossed the line by way of his vineyard, guided by one of his workers. Once I made it to the Free Zone, I would meet back up with the farmer at an agreed-upon location. From there, we would travel to a nearby farm owned by one of his friends, after which the farmer would return home and I would carry on my journey. It sounded like a solid plan.

Once we had worked out the details, while drinking a couple of glasses of wine from Emile's secret stash, it was time to bid farewell to Jean-Francois. I thanked the friendly baker for his hospitality and promised him that I would return after the end of the war to try his famous *Canelés de Bordeaux* when there was once again an abundance of butter flowing through his bakery.

After Jean-Francois's departure, Emile showed me where I would be staying for the next few days.

Because it was fairly common for German soldiers to unexpectedly come by the vineyards, I would have to remain well hidden throughout my entire stay. I wasn't surprised when Emile led me down a stairwell into the basement. We entered the dark cellar and I immediately felt a blanket of cool and humid air surround me.

It's going to be a chilly few days, I thought.

Emile handed me a kerosene lamp and told me to follow him. The cellar was quite large, covering the entire footprint of the house above. Emile proudly told me that the property had been in his family for over two centuries. Although his grapes were processed at a nearby winemaker, looking around the basement, there was no doubt what business Emile was in. There were empty bottles and old farm equipment everywhere.

At the back of the main cellar, there was a hidden entryway to a second room. It was here that the vintner had been able to save his most precious bottles as well as a personal supply of wine to, if necessary, last him through several more years of war. The little back room was also where I would be staying. An army-style cot had been set up between some barrels of wine. I was glad to see three neatly folded blankets on top of the cot. There was no doubt I would need all three. Before leaving me in my hiding place, Emile handed me a corkscrew and told me I could help myself to a bottle of 1939. It had been his best year of the past decade, he boasted.

I opened the bottle and poured myself a small nightcap before going to bed.

A baker, a vintner, and a pastor. What an amazing group of hosts, I thought, as I settled in for my third night away from home.

It took a few days before Emile had everything sorted out with his friend in Langon. With not much else to do, I spent the majority of my time resting and reading the book that Marie had allowed me to hang on to.

On my fourth day in hiding, Emile finally brought down some news instead of just food and water.

We would hit the road the next day, making the 85 kilometer journey to Langon. Traveling at night, past curfew, was more risky than traveling during the day, which is why we decided to leave in the morning. We would travel by truck, under the excuse of transporting empty wine crates to the vineyard where I would be staying at next. The chances of running into a German convoy were small, but just in case, I would hide in the back of the truck between the barrels.

We loaded the truck first thing in the morning and left right after sunrise. I had a spot in the back of the truck hidden between three empty barrels. Emile instructed me to quickly hide inside one of the empty barrels if we made any unexpected stops.

It was a bumpy and long ride navigating through small country roads, but luckily we didn't encounter any German patrols, so I was able to avoid any time inside of an empty wine barrel.

We arrived in Langon in the early afternoon and were welcomed by Emile's friend, Thierry, with a lunch of baguettes, goat cheese and the most delicious quince jam.

Thierry's property was quite a lot larger than that of Emile. His vines surrounded his centrally located house for as far as I could see in all directions.

It was funny to think that somewhere not too far away was the demarcation line, and upon it, unoccupied France.

As we sat outside, enjoying our lunch in perfect spring weather, for a second it was easy to forget that there was a war going on. After four days underground, the warmth of the sun on my face felt heavenly.

All too quickly it was back to reality as we started discussing the plan. Things would happen almost exactly as Emile had outlined several days prior when he first spoke to me about his idea for crossing the demarcation line.

Pending any unexpected delays, I would be crossing into the Free Zone the following day.

Thierry unfolded a map of his property and the surrounding areas that covered almost the entire table. On the map, he showed me exactly where I would be crossing the demarcation line and where I would go from there to meet up with Thierry after he had crossed the checkpoint.

One of Thierry's workers, Alex, would guide me the first 5 kilometers through the vines. From there, I would have to find the meeting point on my own. Since it was too dangerous for me to carry a map, in case we were stopped by a German patrol, I would have to study the map closely this evening and rely on my intuition and several landmarks to reach the small roadside chapel where Thierry and I planned to meet back up. There were five landmarks I had to memorize and find to successfully find Thierry. It felt a bit like a boy scout exercise from when I was a kid, but this time the stakes were much higher.

After lunch it was time for Emile to head back to Bordeaux and I bid farewell to the third host of my journey.

I spent the night at Thierry's sleeping in yet another basement, this time a real wine cellar. The walls of the cellar were lined with racks that would have typically been filled with bottles of wine but now sat mostly empty. I felt for my host, whose business had suffered so deeply since the start of the invasion.

Before turning off my lamp, I took one last look at the map of the property and ran through all the landmarks I needed to pass in order to find Thierry. For the first time since the day of my departure, I felt a little nervous, but more than anything, I felt excited about the adventure of the following day.

I woke up to yet another beautiful spring day in southern France. The sun was slowly rising over the vines as drops of morning dew rolled off the growing grape leaves. The weather was ideal for a long walk through the countryside, but it also meant that there were likely to be more patrols out guarding the demarcation line.

Alex had already arrived when Thierry came to retrieve me from the wine cellar. We all had a cup of coffee and agreed that now was as good a time as any to head out.

Alex, who couldn't have been much older than fifteen, had been helping out at the vineyard since he was a young boy. He proudly told me that he knew the property like the back of his hand and I immediately felt confident to have an excellent guide in him.

We left the house and headed straight into the vines. It was late April and although the grapes were only just starting to form, the leaves on the vines were already thick and provided plenty of cover from any onlooker. The only problem was the height of the greenery, at about 1.50 meter high, our heads popped out over the vines if we stood up tall.

"No need to worry about crouching down the first few kilometers," Alex told me. "But once we get a little closer to the line, we'll need to make sure not to stick out too much."

I followed my young guide as he took me left and right through the plantation. After just a few minutes of walking, I had lost sight of the house and felt like I was in a maze. There was nothing identifiable to give me a sense of direction, but Alex seemed to know exactly where we were going. We walked in silence for about an hour until Alex turned around and instructed me to continue more cautiously.

"We're about 500 meters from the crossing, Leo." he whispered. "Try to make as little noise as possible and make sure to stay low."

He had been just in time with his instructions as not even 100 meters further we suddenly heard voices coming from the west.

Alex stopped, turned around and signaled at me to stop and crouch down. He made himself as small as he could and pressed his back up against a vine, hiding most of his body below the bottom foliage. I followed his example.

I could hear the voices approaching us as I held my breath while my heart started beating rapidly inside my chest. I counted three voices, but by the sound of the footsteps there must have been at least four of them.

I looked at the vines ahead of me and counted twelve rows of plants between us and the path on which the soldiers were patrolling. I knew that if they would look directly into our row, it was impossible for them to miss us. All I could hope for was that their attention would be focussed elsewhere.

The footsteps were now mere meters away as their conversation continued. I didn't dare look at the path and instead focused my eyes on a snail that had slowly started making its way up my hand, leaving behind a trail of slime.

I fought the urge to shiver at its cold and gooey feel on my skin.

I counted one, two, three, and finally a fourth pair of footsteps passing by. As the last officer passed, I finally gathered my nerves, looked up and stole a glimpse of a perfectly polished army boot disappearing from my vision.

We're in the clear, I thought, but then suddenly the last officer's footsteps halted.

I held my breath as my heart almost beat out of my chest.

I felt sure that he had noticed us. My mind started racing through possible scenarios. I carefully listened, waiting for him to turn and the footsteps to grow louder.

Do I fight or do I run? I wondered anxiously as my mind was going a thousand miles an hour.

Suddenly I heard the familiar sound of a lighter being flicked open.

He's lighting a cigarette, I thought, as a wave of relief came over me. His steps resumed and I slowly let out my breath but stayed still for a bit longer. Finally, several minutes after the soldiers had passed, I lifted the snail off my hand, gently placing it on the ground, and got up from my hiding place.

My eyes met those of Alex, but neither of us dared say a word.

He signaled at me to stay back as he went to the path to make sure all was clear.

There were no further patrols in sight, and I joined my guide for the final few meters of occupied France.

Alex halted at the next path we crossed and told me that we had reached the demarcation line and it was time for me to continue on my own.

"This is it?" I asked, surprised. There was nothing to indicate the difference between one side and the other—no barricade, no fence, not even any markings.

"Yes," Alex replied. "It's as simple as that. Cross the path and you're in the Free Zone. Go straight for another 300 meters and you'll see the well on your right, your first landmark. You know where to go from there."

It was hard to comprehend that just a couple of kilometers to the west there was an official checkpoint with soldiers and required documents. Yet here, in the middle of a vineyard, I could cross a simple sand path and reach the same territory.

I hugged Alex goodbye. After our close call, a simple handshake seemed too impersonal. I thanked him for safely guiding me to this point, then crossed the path and left Occupied France behind me.

Luckily, my memory didn't let me down and after passing four more landmarks and another full hour of walking, I found the chapel where Thierry and I had agreed to meet.

I was the first one to arrive. To avoid looking out of place on the side of the road, I entered the chapel and sat down in the back. Twice in one week I had found myself inside a house of worship. What a rare occurrence for me, I thought.

It felt good to be off my feet for a minute, but I didn't get to rest long as Thierry entered the chapel less than ten minutes after my arrival.

"Leo, you made it!" The slight hint of surprise in his voice made me wonder if there were more soldiers patrolling the demarcation line than they had initially led me to believe.

I told him about our narrow escape as we drove to my next guesthouse.

For some reason or another, Thierry's friend who I was supposed to stay with had informed him last minute that I wasn't welcome after all. Instead, I would now be staying with a family friend, an older lady who had recently been widowed and was living by herself in a county house just outside of town.

Madame Renard was a very sweet lady who was happy to have some company and talked my ear off from the second I got there until the second I left. She served me several meals that were so delicious that you would think that she'd had an unlimited pantry of ingredients to choose from, instead of the severely limited wartime selection that was available.

She definitely took great care of me, but the problem was that she didn't have any contacts further along my route that could be of any assistance to me. For the first time since leaving Belgium, I would have to figure out my next step on my own. And wherever I decided to go, there would be no host family waiting to welcome me with a hot meal and a comfortable place to stay.

I spent two days at Madame Renard's being spoiled like a long-lost grandchild while mostly peering over the map of France, trying to figure out the best route to continue my journey on.

I settled on Pau as my next stop. Wanting to cross the Pyrenees on the Mediterranean side, at some point, I needed to start making my way east. Pau was 150 kilometers straight south from Langon, but there was a good train connection, and from there I could start traveling east.

Apart from having run out of contacts, there was another shortage I was starting to face. Once I had purchased my train ticket to Pau, I was almost completely out of spending money.

Back in Belgium, Captain Lentz had repeatedly pressed the importance of making sure to hang on to enough money to be able to pay for a guide when it was time to cross the Pyrenees. Without a guide, there was no chance that I would make it to Spain on my own, he had warned me. I knew that I needed to set aside about 5,500 francs, the equivalent of almost two months' worth of wages, for that purpose.

On the train to Pau, I counted what was left of my money. Not taking into account the money needed to pay the guide, I came to the conclusion that things would get rather tight if I needed to pay for train tickets, food and now accommodations too.

I might have to get creative pretty soon, I thought.

I deboarded the train in Pau and for the first time I really didn't know where to go. It was still early in the afternoon and a beautiful day. With nowhere to go, I left the station and started strolling around the city. I followed the river towards the center of town.

In the middle of the city, rising high above its surroundings, stood Pau's famous medieval castle with its massive rectangular tower, which stood in stark contrast with the rest of the castle's elegant architecture. The city itself was located only 50 kilometers from the Spanish border.

At the horizon, the peaks of the Pyrenees penetrated the clouds in the background of the cityscape. I stood staring at the mountain rage in the distance, the thought of the Spanish border being so close by, yet so hard to reach filled me with frustration. I loosened my gaze from the snow-covered peaks and continued on along the *Boulevard des Pyrenees*.

Despite the beautiful day and my nice surroundings, I was feeling a bit deflated from aimlessly wandering around when I stumbled upon a colorful poster outside a small storefront in the center of town.

It was a recruiting poster for the foreign legion, depicting several men in full uniform patched over each other with the words *"Légion Etrangère"* across the top and down the side of the poster. I was standing there thinking the uniforms looked quite silly, with their red tasseled shoulder pads and hats that looked like wheels of white cheese balancing on the soldiers' heads, when a man behind me spoke out.

"We're always looking for young men like yourself to join the foreign legion," he said.

I turned around to find an older man in uniform, this one without flashy shoulder pads or funky hat.

I politely told him that I wasn't interested, but he wouldn't let me off the hook that easily.

"Hear me out," he insisted. "Come to the office, let me tell you a little bit more about the foreign legion, and I promise I will buy you lunch once we're done talking."

Lunch. He had said the one word that could have possibly triggered my interest. My stomach had been growling for hours now, but I was trying to save money and had decided to skip lunch and instead opt only for an early dinner. Free lunch, however, sounded much more appealing.

"It can't hurt to be informed, I guess," I said and followed him back to his office.

The recruitment office was nothing more than a small room with two desks and more colorful Foreign Legion posters on the wall. The man told me to take a seat across from the first desk. His coworker must have been out hunting for more recruits as the other desk was empty.

He went straight into his pitch to try to convince me to join.

His big sales argument was that by joining the Foreign Legion, I would get to travel the world. Visit places that I would normally never in my life have a chance to visit.

I didn't know a whole lot about the French Foreign Legion, but I knew enough to know that its soldiers weren't exactly sitting on a beach in the tropics staring at a beautiful sunset every evening. The type of traveling he was alluding to involved being shot at in the middle of the North African desert while being eaten alive by sand fleas. Not the type of world traveling I had in mind.

I nodded repeatedly throughout his lengthy pitch and feigned interest by asking just enough questions to ensure the recruiter wouldn't change his mind on his lunch offer.

After almost twenty minutes, he finally finished talking.

Time for lunch, I thought. But instead of getting up to grab his coat, he grabbed a piece of paper from the desk behind him and put it in front of me.

"Acte D'Engagement" it said in all caps at the top of the page.

It was a form to make my enlistment in the Foreign Legion official.

There wasn't a single hair on my head that considered actually joining.

I considered getting up and walking out, giving up on lunch, but I was starving.

"I'm really quite hungry, sir. How about we leave the paperwork for when we get back from lunch?" I tried.

"Oh, don't be silly, Leo," he countered. "It's a short form, it won't take but a minute to complete. Just fill it out, then we can go enjoy our lunch without having to think about it anymore."

He saw the doubtful look set in on my face.

"How about this," he was gearing up for one last attempt. "Fill out the paperwork now, and I will let you hang on to it throughout lunch until we get back to the office."

I wasn't crazy about the idea of filling out potentially binding paperwork that could result in me being shipped off to Africa, but I felt confident that I'd be able to get rid of the recruiter before ever setting foot back into this office, so I reluctantly agreed.

I filled out the one-page contract, committing to serve for at least three years.

My heart skipped a beat when the recruiter stamped and signed the bottom of the form.

In a wave of panic I imagined him keeping the document, men rushing in through the backdoor to drag me away. But, as promised, with a polite smile and a quick nod, he handed the paper back to me. I reached for it in relief, folded it in four and shoved it deep into my back pocket.

We walked to a nearby cafe located at the end of a small alleyway off the central market square.

"Order anything you'd like, Leo," the recruiter said. "Good meals will be hard to come by once you're abroad."

The ink of my signature had only just dried, and all of a sudden the recruiter started sounding a lot more realistic about what my time in the foreign legion might look like. Talk of sunsets and world travel made way for tips on keeping sand out of my boots and making sure to protect my skin from the ever-burning sun.

If I'd had any desire at all to join the Foreign Legion, it would have undoubtedly been gone after the personal experience stories he shared over our lunch of chicken stew.

He might have let go of the false portrayal of the Foreign Legion experience, but he hadn't given up on trying to get a hold of my paperwork. He asked me twice during lunch if I wanted him to hold on to my form to ensure safekeeping.

This guy might not be as easy to get rid of as I had hoped, I thought, as I excused myself and walked over to the bathroom at the back of the cafe.

I could probably outrun him, but then I didn't know the city as well as he did. What I definitely didn't want to do was use violence to make my escape, but if absolutely necessary, I would.

I was in the bathroom, going over various scenarios in my head, when I suddenly noticed the small window above the toilet as I was washing my hands. It looked to be just big enough for me to fit through.

This was quite literally my window of opportunity.

Without hesitation, I quickly climbed on top of the toilet seat, one foot on each side of the toilet bowl, and opened the little window. After sneaking a peak outside to make sure the coast was clear, I hosted myself up and through the opening.

I was hanging halfway out of the window when I realized the true challenge would be the landing. Without enough space to maneuver myself around, I would just have to hope for the best.

I extended my arms outwards and tried to lower myself down as slowly as possible. I was still a solid half a meter above ground when my legs flung out of the window, gravitating over my head as my body was pushed into an accidental summer salt. I smacked down on the ground but had somehow managed to avoid any real injuries other than a few scrapes. I stood up, wiped the dust off my coat and walked back up the alley as if nothing had happened. Luckily, nobody had seen my inelegant escape. I snuck a quick peek through the restaurant window, where I saw that the recruiter was still patiently waiting for my return from the bathroom.

I grinned and calmly walked in the other direction.

I didn't want to continue walking the streets any longer than needed, just in case I'd run into the recruiter again. As soon as I felt far enough away from the restaurant, I entered the first guesthouse with a *Chambres Libres* sign out front and booked a room for the night. I had a full stomach, and despite having to pay a small fee for it, a proper bed to sleep on. I couldn't help but smile at the thought of my sneaky escape. I just wish I could have seen the look on the recruiter's face when he finally figured out that I wasn't coming back.

I planned to take the earliest train out of Pau the next morning, and get as far away from the Foreign Legion recruiting office as I possibly could.

I made it to the Pau train station without any issues. As I put my train ticket in my back pocket, I noticed the enlistment form that was still safely tucked away.

I considered ripping it up into small pieces and throwing it away, but then for some reason I decided to hang on to it. A small souvenir of my brief time in the French Foreign Legion, I thought.

In hindsight though, it would have been much safer to discard the form as I later on learned that deserting from the Foreign Legion is punishable by death. With a signed application form in my possession, I was technically a deserter, even without ever having spent one second in uniform.

By the time Pau was waking up and lines outside of bakeries were forming, I was on my way, finally heading east.

My next goal was to make it to Perpignan. According to Colonel Lentz, the southeastern city, located in the Pyrenees-Oriental, was the best place to find a reliable guide to help me cross the mountain range and enter Spain.

In a hurry to get out of Pau, I bought a ticket on the first long-haul train to depart the station. Unfortunately, this ended up being a train to Toulouse.

Toulouse was further east, alright, but it was also more north, which felt like a bit of a step in the wrong direction.

I was dreading getting to Toulouse and finding myself in the same situation as I did upon arrival in Pau, host-less, purposeless and almost penniless, but as it turned out, there must have been a reason I stepped on that particular train after all.

Sitting across from me was a young man. He was a bit peculiar looking, with red hair and bushy eyebrows that stood in stark contrast with his other boyish facial features. I had politely greeted him when I first sat down, then I had turned my attention to what was happening out of the window. Five minutes later, the train departed, and I settled in for the long journey. But by the time we had reached full cruising speed, I couldn't shake the feeling of being watched.

I turned my head and sure enough, the young man was staring straight at me.

I shot him a questioning glance, which was all he needed. He took it as an open invitation to start speaking and managed to talk non stop for the next four halts.

Not that I had the opportunity to squeeze in a single word, but I was speechless at his ability to hold a thirty minute conversation with only the occasional nod in response.

He told me about where he was heading, where he grew up, his opinion about the war, what his plans were for the future, you name it, he told me about it.

Finally, he asked about me and paused.

"I'm heading to Perpignan," I said. "Toulouse was the only train leaving Pau this morning that was heading even remotely in the right direction, so I guess that's where I'm going first."

My curt reply threw him off for a second or two, but then off he went again.

I was seriously considering getting up and finding myself a new seat, but suddenly the endless string of words started to sound a lot more interesting.

The young man, who had by now had introduced himself to me as Philippe, offered for me to stay with him once we got to Toulouse. Even better, he would be heading to Marseille the following day with his uncle and offered for me to go with them.

Marseille was about 300 kilometers up the coast from Perpignan, but it was a city that was home to one of the safe houses that Colonel Lentz had told me about, so it would undoubtedly be worth the detour.

After being at my own mercy for a few days, it would be good to receive some guidance.

I let Philippe yap on a little longer before eventually shutting him down with the excuse of feeling extremely tired and wanted to take a brief nap.

I don't typically fall asleep quickly, but at the pure joy of silence, I dozed off almost as soon as I closed my eyes.

Philippe's uncle came to meet us at the station. From there, we traveled to a small town just east of Toulouse where we spent the night. The following morning, we hit the road bright and early in the uncle's old Citroën truck.

We shuffled along small country roads, making it to Carcassonne by mid afternoon where we stopped for the night.

The following day was the longer part of our journey. We left before sunrise and spent the entire day slowly making our way east.

When we were still on the train, I wondered if Philippe's uncle would be a talker just like his nephew. Sure enough, it must have run in the family. The two of them combined didn't stop talking for more than twenty seconds for the entire two days of the journey. By the time I stepped out of the car in Marseille, I thought my head might explode.

I had asked for them to drop me at the Seamen's Mission near the Vieux-Port.

I thanked the talkative duo for the ride and their companionship and waved goodbye as the old truck drove off.

After taking a minute to enjoy the silence while taking in the cool breeze coming from the ocean, I walked up to the front door of *46 Rue de Forbin* and gave it a short but firm knock.

The door opened just enough for me to make out a spectacled greying man with a long beard peering at me from behind the door.

"Can I help you?" he proclaimed, his question sounding more like a statement than an inquiry.

"I've been traveling from Belgium," I cautiously started. "I was told by a contact back home that this would be a safe place for me to find shelter for the night."

"Contact name?"

In a matter of two words, he had somehow managed to get even less personable.

"Colonel Lentz," I replied, keeping my answer just as short.

My answer must have been satisfactory as the door slowly opened and I was gestured to come inside. Without another word, the man started walking down a dark hallway.

Somehow, after spending two days with the most talkative men in France, it seemed that I had managed to find the least talkative one.

I followed the man down the hallway until we reached a brightly lit kitchen standing out from the darkness. Inside were three men, sitting around a table, cups of tea in front of them.

The man sat down at the only open chair and left me standing awkwardly in front of them.

Two of the men must have been around my age. Their identical haircuts and freckled faces said more about them than they probably would have liked. There was no doubt in my mind that they were English pilots in the process of being smuggled back to the U.K..

The third man at the table was probably in his late thirties, he had an inviting face and his hair was brushed to one side.

He addressed me in French, but with a clear English accent to it, asking me who I was and how I had arrived here. After giving him some background on my story and details on how I had ended up at the Seamen's Mission, he instructed the man who had opened the door for me to find me a chair.

The friendly looking man introduced himself as Donald Caskie, he was a Scottish pastor who was in charge of the place.

My observations on the first two men were proven to be right. The other two men were indeed British RAF pilots. Their plane had been shot down above the south of Belgium a couple weeks prior. They had been lucky to find some locals willing to help them out and had been passed along from safe house to safe house over the past few days until they had reached Marseille. From here, they would travel on by boat to Gibraltar from where they would be sent back to England.

Unfortunately, it was immediately made clear that there was no room for me on that boat. A direct line like that was a luxury only granted to soldiers in need of quickly rejoining their units. What I did get was a place to stay, a couple of meals and an address to a cafe in Perpignan where I could likely find a guide to help me cross the Pyrenees.

I spent the evening listening to the pilots' stories about their adventures in the RAF. I couldn't wait to make it to England myself to start making my own memories.

With no further reason to stay in Marseille, the following day I started my travels down the Mediterranean coastline to Perpignan.

Trying to save money, I decided to make my way south by hitchhiking and walking.

I left the Seamen's Mission and walked over to the nearby harbor. I figured that fishermen and seafarers would be more likely than the average citizen to give a ride to a refugee. Plus, knowing something about the ship chandler business could help me start a conversation.

Arriving at the harbor, I saw a group of five men standing on the dock near a fishing boat that must have just returned from sea.

Perfect, I thought, and walked over to them.

"Any luck, gentlemen?"

They paused their conversation and looked over at me.

The oldest one of the group took a step towards me. He had a cigarette dangling from the side of his mouth that seemingly magically stayed in place while he spoke.

"You need something?"

His tone made it clear that there was little chance that he would assist me with anything. Still, I asked if anyone happened to be driving south who I could hitch a ride with.

"Bugger off, kid." he replied drily, and turned around.

Not exactly the warm welcome that I was hoping for.

I walked away and tried my luck with the next group of men I saw standing ashore.

After four more unsuccessful tries, I was starting to doubt my method. Maybe I should just get out of Marseille and from there try hitchhiking the traditional way, I thought.

At the end of the harbor, I saw a young man standing by himself, and decided to give it a final try.

"Hi there," I said.

He looked up from the magazine that he was browsing through and acknowledged me with a slight smile.

A smile was more than I got from any of the other guys, I thought, before jumping into my pitch.

"I'm waiting for a friend to come pick me up," he said, once I had finished. "He's taking me to somewhere just outside of Montpellier. If he has space and it's okay by him, you're welcome to join."

I thankfully agreed.

A few minutes later, the man's friend showed up in a black Peugeot 402, looking quite out of place in the harbor. Clearly not a fisherman himself, he looked more like a banker or a businessman. The two together made for an unlike duo, but the man was kind enough to offer me a ride, so I didn't ask any questions.

Montpellier was about half-way to Perpignan. Getting a single ride that took me half-way to my destination was more than I could have hoped for. I gratefully settled in in the back of the car as we started our road trip.

We parted ways just past Montpellier. The men were heading north, to a small village nearby, whereas I had decided to stay on the main road, where I was more likely to find another ride.

I thanked the fisherman and his friend for helping me, and continued my journey on foot.

At first, I didn't mind the walk. I had been sitting down for hours and it felt nice to stretch my legs and get some fresh air.

Each time the sound of a car engine emerged from the background, I would stick out my thumb in the hope of getting a ride, but after an hour of walking not a single car had stopped.

The temperature was starting to drop, and soon the sun would set. More urgently than a ride, I needed to find a place to sleep.

There was a small settlement of farmhouses in the distance that I decided to target. I felt confident that at least one of the farmers would give me a place to spend the night.

By the time I made it to the farms, my stomach was growling, and it was almost completely dark out.

The first door I knocked on closed as quickly as it had opened. As soon as the farmer heard that my accent wasn't local, he told me to get off his property.

Moving on to the second farm, almost the exact same thing happened. The farmer threatened to call the police if he ever saw me again.

There was one farm left for me to hopefully find a place to stay for the night. I walked over to the final residence and knocked on the door. I waited for over a minute, but despite the light burning behind the windows, the front door never opened.

Clearly, they didn't want any guests either.

I was walking back towards the main road, contemplating where I was going to sleep, when I saw a barn at the edge of the property.

Perfect, I thought.

I plowed through a field, careful not to trip over any sleeping cows, arriving at the barn, which luckily was unlocked.

The barn was filled with bales of hay, which would serve perfectly fine as a bed for the night. My stomach was still growling and it was colder than I would have liked, but at least I had a roof above my head.

My hunger woke me early the next morning, thankfully before the farmer had a chance to discover his unwanted guest.

If I had another long day of walking ahead, I needed to find some food. I looked around the barn, but all I could see were bales of hay and some tools.

It would be too risky to go looking for food closer to the farms.

I was about to give up and head out, when I heard the sound of a rooster crowing.

Where there are roosters, there must be chicken, I thought.

I walked out of the barn and discovered a chicken pen nearby. I cautiously walked over and grabbed one of the eggs from an empty nest.

Scrambled eggs or an omelet sounded delicious, but the thought of a raw egg on an empty stomach was far from mouth-watering.

But, I needed the energy.

As I cracked open the egg, some of the egg white came oozing over the side of the shell, the gooey liquid dripping on to my hand.

I took a deep breath, closed my nose and slurped down the egg.

Surprisingly, not that bad, I thought, and decided to grab two more eggs for the road.

By the time the sun rose over the French countryside, I was back on the main road heading towards Perpignan.

After a few kilometers of walking, a friendly merchant picked me up.

Unlike the previous day, my day was filled with many short rides and lots of walking. Still, I made it to my destination by nightfall.

I arrived in Perpignan on April 6, 1941, exactly two weeks after leaving home.

CHAPTER THREE

Crossing the Pyrenees

A rmed with an address for where to find a guide and with enough money in my pocket to pay for one, I was feeling confident upon my arrival in Perpignan.

Perpignan was a cozy Mediterranean city, nestled between the ocean and the mountains, and with the April spring weather that brought its citizens outside, the town radiated a pleasant feel. It was the type of place I wouldn't have minded spending some more extensive time if it wasn't for the war or the urgency to cross the border before things in France took a turn for the worse.

The cafe I had been told to go to was located on the *Place de la Revolution*, not far from the city's cathedral.

It was late morning when I arrived at the cafe. One of the staff members was still setting up the patio as I entered the small inside area. The cafe must have only just opened for the day as I looked to be the first customer. Not wanting to jump right into the real reason for why I was here, I went up to the old man who was standing behind the bar and ordered a cup of coffee.

The man slowly walked over to the coffee machine, went through the necessary steps and returned with a cup of weak but warm liquid.

For being someone who worked at, and most likely owned, a cafe, I didn't get the impression that he was very personable. Not feeling all too sure on how to approach the situation, I took my cup of coffee and sat down at a nearby table.

I was feeling unsure about the old man, but reminded myself that I had been given this address for a reason, and by a trustworthy source.

As I was finishing up my cup, the man walked over.

"Can I get you another coffee?" he asked when he reached my table.

"No, but I hear I might be able to find some help here to cross into Spain," I said, taking a bit of a risk.

I was expecting a sense of surprise from the old man, but my comment didn't seem to throw him off at all. Not a single muscle in his face had moved.

"Come back at 5, ask for Pierre," he said, then turned around and shuffling back to the bar.

I left the little cafe feeling sure that I was on the right track to securing a guide. With quite a bit of time to kill before having to be back at the cafe, I walked around the city, this time avoiding any posters recruiting men to join the Foreign Legion, or any other armed forces for that matter.

I couldn't have asked for a more beautiful day to explore the city and was feeling quite relaxed after what I considered having been a successful morning. Time went by fairly quickly and before I knew it, it was time to head back to the *Place de la Revolution*.

It was just after 5 p.m. when I found myself at the cafe once again. The tables and chairs that were just being set up when I had been there in the morning were now almost all filled with people. The topics of customer conversations might have been a bit more serious than just a few years prior, but all in all, people in Perpignan seemed to be going about their regular routines as much as they could.

The inside of the cafe was now filled with smoke and conversation. I tried to find the old man I had spoken to in the morning, but failing to locate him, I approached a young girl who was balancing a tray of empty glasses on one hand as she hastily walked towards the back of the establishment.

"Pardon me, I'm looking for Pierre," I said, trying to speak loud enough for her to understand me while avoiding drawing any attention to me.

"Guy with the mustache, at the end of the bar," she replied, using her empty hand to point at a dark-haired man who was sitting at the bar, bent over the evening paper.

I turned to thank her, but she had already rushed off, so I moved towards the bar and approached the man, strategically positioned myself to his left with my back turned towards his closest neighbor.

I got right to the point.

"Pierre, I've heard you're the person I need to speak to."

He put down his paper and looked me right in the eye.

"Let's take this conversation outside, shall we?" he said, immediately catching on to my reason for being there.

We left the crowded cafe and walked out into the cool evening air. It was still light out, but the cobblestoned streets were practically empty. As we walked away from the cafe Pierre lit a cigarette, waiting until we were completely out of hearing distance before he started to speak. He wasted no words, getting straight to the facts.

"My price is 5,500 francs," he said, then released a steady stream of smoke from his pursed together lips while looking me straight in the eyes, as if he expected me to be shocked at the price.

I gave him a quick nod, after which he continued.

"I wait until I have at least two people to guide to make it worth my time. We will leave from Banyuls, you will stay at a friend of mine's house there until it is time to leave. I ask for 1,500 francs up front, before I take you to Banyuls, the remainder has to be paid by the time we set out for the crossing."

"Fair enough," I said. "I will pay you the first 1,500 when you come to collect me to go to your friend's house."

We spent a couple of minutes going over a few details, but rather quickly everything was agreed on.

Pierre shook my hand and left me with a last piece of advice.

"Oh, and Leo, make sure you have a good pair of shoes," he looked down at my footwear, threw his cigarette bud to the side, then turned around and walked off.

As Pierre walked away, I found myself looking down at my shoes alone in the street in the middle of Perpignan.

They were a nice pair of shoes, brown leather, tight laces, classy. They had been a gift for my eighteenth birthday. When I was working for my father I used to switch between this pair and a similar style black pair depending on what color suit I wore. Every evening, after returning from the office, I would clean off any dirt and polish them with shoeshine to make sure they were in pristine condition for the next day.

Even on the road I had tried to keep them clean, wiping them off with warm water and a piece of cloth every chance I got.

They could use a shine though, I thought.

More concerningly, they might have been great shoes to walk around the city and hadn't been an issue during my long walk through the vineyards, but they definitely weren't hiking boots. After the fee I would have to pay Pierre, hiking boots weren't exactly in the budget, so my smart city shoes would have to do.

As agreed, Pierre came to meet me the following afternoon at the guesthouse where I spent the night. I paid him the deposit and off we went to Banyuls-sur-Mer, a small coastal town about an hour's drive south of Perpignan, located just 10 kilometers from the Spanish border.

Pierre's friends lived in a small chalet that looked like it belonged at the foothills of a more northern mountain range, like the Alps instead of the Pyrenees. Their house itself was simple, but the view was breathtaking.

The chalet overlooked the green outskirts of the Pyrenees, many slopes of which were covered with grapevines, then in the distance the hills morphed into the ocean, a subtle transition from green to blue like the paints in a watercolor, flowing through each other.

As it turned out, Pierre had already found a second person to guide across the mountains. When I entered the kitchen, a young man who thanks to the wide-eyed questioning expression on his face, didn't look like he was part of the family, was sitting at the kitchen table. He stood up, introduced himself to me as Louis, and sat back down. At Pierre's instruction, I took the empty seat beside him.

"We likely won't leave tonight," Pierre explained. "I need to gather some intel, make sure there won't be any unexpected surprises along the way when we head out. Make yourselves comfortable and get some rest, you'll need the energy for the climb."

Our guide promised to return within a matter of days and left Louis and I alone with our hosts.

We were fed a simple meal of potato soup and were shown to a small windowless room that the two of us would share, and where we were supposed to stay until Pierre returned.

Our hosts were friendly enough, but didn't seem interested in getting to know either of us, so for the next three days, Louis and I spent our time playing cards and getting acquainted with one another.

As soon as our hosts left the two of us alone, Louis set the tone for the next few days.

"Are you planning on having Franco over for drinks as soon as we cross into Spain?" he laughed, eying my freshly cleaned dress shoes.

If it wasn't for his big smile and lighthearted tone, I would have taken offense, but Louis was the type of guy who you couldn't help but immediately like.

I was amazed at his positivity and kind spirit, especially after hearing his story.

Louis was a young fisherman from Dunkirk who had lost his boat when the Germans bombed the beach during the British evacuation. Much worse, he had lost his best friend that day, another angler who was assisting British soldiers by helping them back across the Channel.

After losing his friend and his income, he had left Dunkirk and had been traveling through France, taking odd jobs left and right to save up money to pay for a guide to cross the Pyrenees, for the better part of the past year.

I had expected time to pass slowly as we waited for Pierre's return, but thanks to good company and a simple deck of cards, the next three days went by much faster than I could have hoped.

It was around 5 p.m. on Thursday when a knock on our door unexpectedly turned out to be Pierre who had returned to tell us to get ready. We would be leaving that same evening.

"There has been an increase of patrols along the coastal route," he told us. "We will have to take a route that takes us further into the mountains. The hike will be a lot tougher, and a lot longer, but we can't risk staying along the sea."

What could have been a hike of just a few hours had now been replaced with a serious trek that would most likely take three or four days. The additional climbing also meant more severe temperature difference. Even in April, it could still get very cold in the higher parts of the Pyrenees. Suddenly, I was feeling a lot less comfortable with this part of the journey.

We were given a final hot meal, then Pierre handed us water flasks and announced that we would be leaving as soon as the sun had fully set. We would be traveling by night and resting during the day to avoid being seen.

Before heading out, Pierre asked us to pay the remainder of our balance. I would have felt more comfortable waiting to pay the balance until safely across the border, but he made a valid point in that he didn't want to be caught traveling back to France carrying such a large sum of money.

"The balance will need to be paid before we leave, or we don't leave."

He stood stoically in front of us, patiently waiting for the two of us to take out our money and pay him.

I didn't like him very much, but I needed him.

"If we run into any guards or police, it's every man for himself," he continued after we had paid him. "If we all get arrested after being separated, you'll act as if you've never seen me before. Any questions?"

Quite the motivational speech, I thought.

Louis and I both shook our heads no, and with that, we were ready to head out.

Around 8:30 p.m., we departed from the chalet and set out for what was to become a long and tough journey.

As opposed to hugging the coast line throughout our hike and remaining in relatively low elevation, as had been the original plan, our alternative route would first take us further inland before heading into the Albera mountain range.

Pierre warned us that there were several peaks over a kilometer high and that conditions would undoubtedly get quite tough.

The biggest challenge of the first few hours of walking was getting accustomed to the darkness. Within thirty minutes of leaving the chalet, there were no more houses in sight and we were stuck with only the moonlight above and Pierre walking ahead to guide us. We started out walking on small farm roads, while occasionally crossing fields and vineyards. It wasn't the toughest terrain, but it took me some time to get used to the uneasiness of not being able to fully see where I was stepping.

Pierre seemed to find it no more difficult than walking in plain daylight, speeding on as Louis and I struggled to keep up with him.

We walked in silence for about two hours until we reached the start of a trail leading into the mountains. Our guide gave us a couple of minutes to rest and have a sip of water before continuing our walk. He warned us that our hike would slowly start becoming more challenging from now on and told us to stay close.

I could feel the steady incline as we inched our way up the hiking trail. We were surrounded by more trees and bushes now, making it even harder to see. My feet were starting to hurt, but I wasn't willing to give in to it just yet. I knew there was a lot of climbing ahead and that it would only get worse. I wondered how Louis was doing behind me, but I was too focussed on making sure my feet were put down stably with each step, while simultaneously trying to avoid getting hit in face by overhanging tree branches, to ask about my friend's wellbeing, so we hiked along in silence.

After several hours of making our way up the mountain, exhaustion started to creep up on me. We hadn't had a break since we had entered the trail and the walk kept getting steeper. To top it off, a steady mist of microscopic raindrops had started to descend on us. The raindrops were so small, it was as if they had been sent down from the heavens specifically to find their way in between the fibers of my clothing. Before long, I was drenched and cold to the bone.

Ahead of me, our guide kept pushing on as if nothing had changed.

As time passed, the rain started coming down more strongly and before long the ground turned into a slippery mess. With every other step, my dress shoe slid out of my footprint. It took all of my concentration and willpower to keep pushing forward.

To make things worse, the cold and humid air along with the physical effort I was putting in had triggered my asthma. I struggled to inhale enough oxygen to keep me going and was wheezing loudly with every breath I released.

At what must have been close to five in the morning, we reached an empty shepherd's cabin where we were to stop and rest throughout the day. The rain was still coming down and by now I was completely drenched. The only positive was that the cold temperature had numbed the pain of the giant blisters that had developed on both my ankles.

I entered the small refuse and found a place to sit down. Looking over at Louis, he seemed to be in just as rough of a shape I was in. We made eye contact, but were both too exhausted to speak.

As Pierre built a fire, I started peeling off my wet layers of clothing. I hesitated when I came to my shoes. I knew that taking them off would feel heavenly, but I also realized that I would be having to put them back on later, the pain of which would almost outweigh the joy of taking them off. I just hoped the warmth of the fire would be strong enough to dry out my shoes and socks before we'd resume our journey.

The wool of my socks stuck to the open wounds that were not just on my ankles but also under my toes as I slowly pulled the fabric down my feet while a burning pain ran through me.

When finally released from my footwear, I plopped down on one of the straw beds in the otherwise almost empty room and didn't move again for the remainder of the morning.

When I woke up from some much needed sleep, I found that Pierre had prepared some porridge for us to eat. The small wood fire had warmed up the entire room, and I was finally feeling a bit more comfortable again.

Louis was still sound asleep on the makeshift bed besides me.

"We'll head back out after dark, in about four hours," our guide said as he handed me a bowl of porridge. "Try to get some more rest, there's more climbing ahead of us."

My wheezing had calmed down, but I was still not breathing with ease. I needed all the rest I could get before heading back out. After filling my stomach, I fell back asleep almost immediately, sleeping soundly until Louis woke me to let me know it was almost time to leave.

My clothes had dried well in front of the fire, but my socks now felt hard as cardboard.

I ripped my handkerchief into several strips of fabric and wrapped them around my feet in the hope of lessening the pain. Luckily, it had stopped raining, so at least we had that going for us.

With the last daylight disappearing in the distance, we embarked on the second day of our journey across the Pyrenees. The air was cooler now that we were at higher altitude but without the rain, and being able to breathe a little better again, it made for an almost pleasant hike.

After a few kilometers of walking, I forgot the pain in my feet and got into the groove of climbing and descending and trying to keep up with Pierre.

Louis seemed to be doing better as well, as we were able to have several brief conversations throughout the night.

At the end of another full night of hiking, we reached a similar shelter for our second night in the mountains. Exhausted from two nights of intense physical activity, I fell asleep within minutes of reaching the cabin.

Once again, I was woken up by Louis, but this time not by a gentle nudge.

"Leo, Leo!" his voice sounded panicked as he was pulling at my arm. "He's gone!"

"Who's gone?" I asked, confused as I rubbed the sleep out of my eyes.

"Our guide!"

I suddenly felt wide awake. I looked over and noticed that Pierre's backpack had disappeared. Louis and I ran outside, but he was nowhere to be seen.

"Let's give him some time. Maybe he just went to scout the area before we head out," I suggested.

After an hour of waiting, and no return from Pierre, it seemed that there was no other conclusion to come to than that our guide had abandoned us.

"What do we do now?" Louis wondered out loud, as he sat on the edge of one of the straw beds with his head in his hands.

"Well, we can't stay here," I said, stating the obvious. "All we know is that Spain is south, so let's just keep walking south. I'm sure that eventually we'll run into something."

We had spent the last hour of the second night slowly descending, so I hoped that we had passed the final peak of the crossing and were now on the flip side of the mountain range.

"Let's head out early," I suggested to Louis. There might be a larger chance of us being seen if we travel by daylight, but we will need the visibility traveling in unknown territory without a guide. The last thing we needed was to be walking in the wrong direction and getting lost without enough food or water.

It was mid-afternoon when we stepped out of the cabin and looked up at the sun to determine our direction.

We decided to walk straight south and reevaluate every couple of hours. Without a guide, we didn't only have to pay more attention to our route, we also had to pay a lot more attention to our surroundings to make sure nobody could see us. We moved along cautiously. The daylight helped, and I felt like we were making decent progress, but without any landmarks to go by there was no telling if we were on the right path or not.

As the sun started to set, we had a decision to make, either we looked for shelter and stopped for the night, or we kept walking. We were more likely to head in the wrong direction during the night, but on the other hand, we were less likely to be seen. We were exhausted and could definitely use the rest, but without a proper shelter to stop at, we were in for an extremely cold night if we stopped now.

We kept pushing on for the time being and agreed only to stop if we happened to stumble upon a shelter.

Throughout the day we had continued our slow descent, and I knew that we couldn't be far from the Spanish border now. If we pushed through, hopefully we could stop and find a place to rest once we were certain to have France and the Pyrenees behind us.

As the night fell, our hike quickly became a lot more challenging. The landscape wasn't the problem, it was more open than at the start of the mountains and there weren't as many climbs and descents, but the darkness made it very hard to stay on track. Without the sun to help determine the direction we were heading in, it was very easy to start doubting ourselves and feeling panicked.

Several times throughout the night we stopped, questioningly looked at each other, then decided to keep moving in the same direction simply because we couldn't think of a good enough reason to change course.

For hours on end we walked through the same heath of high grass, boulders and the occasional pine tree. We wouldn't have noticed if we were walking in circles since, as far as we could see, everything looked the same.

Finally, after a long and exhausting night of walking, the sun started to rise. We decided to sit down for a few minutes, have a drink of water and rest for a moment.

We were almost out of water, which could quickly become a problem if we weren't able to find inhabited territory soon. Even with the first daylight now bringing a golden shine to the Pyrenees, I still couldn't make out any houses on the horizon.

"Let's not rest here too long," Louis cautioned. "There's nowhere we can hide if anyone sees us and it will only get tougher to get back up if we wait much longer."

I knew he was right, but it felt so great to be off my feet for a moment. If I would have closed my eyes, I would have undoubtedly fallen asleep right then and there. I dragged myself back up on my feet and took a moment to take in the beauty of the cotton candy colored sunrise, before continuing our march.

After two more hours of walking with no change in sight, I started to really feel concerned.

"What if we are walking in the wrong direction, Louis," I pondered out loud. "What if we're no closer to Spain than we were when Pierre abandoned us?"

"You can't think like that. We have no choice but to keep going," he sighed, not sounding very convincing.

Along with our morale, our pace had also taken a hit. Since our last break, our speed had decreased significantly. I could barely feel my legs and was too tired to count how many hours it had been since I had last slept.

I tried to block out any negative thoughts, hiding the idea of being lost and falling without water in a far corner of my brain, and focused instead on the simple movement of setting one foot in front of the other.

Despite the exhaustion, we pushed on some more.

Then, just as I was considering dropping down and taking a nap right there in the middle of the moorland, Louis spotted something moving at the bottom of the hill.

"Look!" he shouted out as he pointed at a series of dots moving along the bottom of the hill.

We counted eight of them, which felt like too many to be mountain guards. We quickly decided to get a little closer to get a better look. We hurried down the hill until we reached a distance we felt safe enough to remain unseen, but close enough to make out details on the men marching below. I couldn't believe my eyes when I saw the men's uniforms. The little tassels on their hats were a typical feature of Belgian uniforms.

"Those are Belgian soldiers!" I exclaimed as soon as I had caught a better look of the men.

Louis shot me a confused look, undoubtedly wondering why on earth Belgian soldiers would be patrolling the Pyrenees, but I was convinced I was right. I could recognize those uniforms from any distance.

"Trust me!" I shouted to my travel companion and started running down the hill.

CHAPTER FOUR

Captivity

As we ran down the hill, quickly approaching the men I felt certain were our allies, I was suddenly overcome with doubt.

The closer we came, the less familiar their uniforms looked.

Maybe I had wanted to run into friendly oncoming traffic so badly that I hadn't used enough caution. Maybe I had seen what I wanted to see, instead of what was really there.

I panicked, I glanced around, but I knew very well there was no place to escape to now. We were in the middle of an open field, there was nowhere to run or hide.

As we came closer, the hats that the men were wearing, that from a distance had looked so much like what I had wanted them to look like, now took on a very distinct shape that looks like typewriter covers. An identifying sign of the Spanish Guardia Civil, and about the last thing I wanted to see after hiking up and down the Pyrenees for three days and nights.

"*Documentados de identification,*" one of the officers shouted harshly once we were within hearing distance, asking to see our papers.

Louis and I stood there completely dumbstruck and still out of breath from running down the hill.

I could feel all hope and excitement draining from me. We both just stood there, too shocked and disheartened to react to the soldier's orders.

The officer ordered one of his men to search us. They took our wallets with what little money was left inside of them after paying for our guide, but of course there were no papers to be found.

Without any further discussion, our hands were forced behind our backs, we were handcuffed and ordered to march.

I looked over at Louis, who shot me an angry look.

Not only had I gotten myself arrested, it was my fault that Louis now found himself in handcuffs. I felt terrible.

As we walked along a sandy trail flanked by the lingering hills of the Pyrenees, I kept trying to think of a way out of the horrible situation I suddenly found myself in.

I was physically and mentally exhausted from crossing the mountains, but not quite ready to give up. My mind was racing, but I couldn't find a way out. We were two prisoners in a group of eight officers. The landscape didn't make for an easy way to get lost from the group, and even if we were able to escape, we had barely been able to survive when our hands were untied, let alone now that we were handcuffed.

We had been marching for about an hour when the moonlike landscape around us slowly started to give way for farms and then some taverns and houses.

We passed a sign that read *"Bienvenido a Figueras."*

At least now I knew where we were, I thought somberly.

By that point, I was more concerned with simply getting somewhere so that I could get off my feet and a lot less with coming up with a way to escape.

We finally arrived at the Figueras police station when the last sun was setting us.

The station was nothing more than a small two-story building located in the center of town. Inside we were told to sit down on a row of chairs across from the receptionist's desk and ordered to wait.

Louis was still angry with me and we were both so exhausted that we didn't even try to speak to each other.

After a few minutes, one of the officers that had been in the group that arrested us appeared from an office and told me to follow him.

I was brought to the chief of police's office to be questioned.

The chief, a tall man in his mid-fifties with a thick black mustache, sat behind a vast antique desk that faced the door. As we walked in he glanced up from his paperwork and told me to take a seat. He sighed, put down his pen and took a better look at me.

I wasn't exactly the first foreigner without papers that had been arrested crossing the Pyrenees, so the interrogation was short. He asked me a couple questions in French about where I was from, why I had been traveling without papers and where I was planning ongoing. Of course, he knew very well that I had been on my way to England, so there was no point in lying. Next they asked me some standard background questions and with that, on April 12, 1941, I was officially booked into the prison of Figueras.

"Welcome to Spain," the chief said as he stamped my paperwork, indicating that the interrogation was over.

The first officer, who was still standing behind me, told me to follow him again.

He led me down a hall of cells that looked like small bare offices with little square windows in the door. I peeked through the windows and could see that the cells were about fifty percent occupied. They had left an empty cell between each prisoner.

About six cells down we came to the second empty cell in a row, which was where we halted. The officer fished a large bundle of keys from his pocket, opened the lock and motioned for me to step inside. I was so exhausted that I almost felt happy just to have a place to rest. But not having eaten all day, I was also starving and figured I would try my luck.

"Can I get something to eat?" I gently asked the guard before stepping into the cell.

He just shrugged and mumbled something about later.

I entered my cell and the officer locked behind me.

My jail cell was a small rectangular room with thick cement walls that had been painted white. There was a window too small to climb through that overlooked the courtyard, and a narrow bed that wasn't much more than a wooden plank on four legs. There weren't any blankets, just a pillow that was filled with straw, still I was happy that I had a place to finally lie down.

There was no point in overthinking things right now. At this moment all I could do was get some rest and hopefully the next day would bring answers. I tried to forget about my growling stomach, tended to my blister-covered feet, then lay down and fell asleep within minutes.

Despite the hard bed, I managed to sleep through the night.

I woke to the sunlight falling in through my tiny window, lighting up my cell. As soon as I opened my eyes, the hunger returned. I looked around my cell in the hope that a guard had brought some food while I was asleep, but to my great disappointment everything looked exactly the same as the previous night.

Sitting alone in my cell, the harsh reality of my arrest started to sink in. With absolutely nothing to distract me, negative thoughts quickly filled my head.

England suddenly felt millions of miles away. I had no idea what was going to happen to me or how long I would be stuck there. With the excitement of the previous day behind me, I now had plenty of time to feel guilty about the mistake I had made running down that hill.

I wondered how Louis was doing, undoubtedly sitting in a similar cell a couple of doors down. He must hate me for mistaking those Guardia Civil agents for Belgian soldiers, I thought.

About an hour after I woke up, a guard finally brought me a piece of bread and some water. I tried to communicate with him in French, but he didn't understand me, or at least he pretended not to. As quickly as he had entered my cell he excited again, locking the door, leaving me to my emptiness.

Without much else to do, I spent the majority of the morning trying to sleep some more. The past few days had been so physically draining that I was able to dose off a couple of times, which helped pass time. The afternoon was filled with more thinking and staring out of the window. I briefly tried to come up with some possible escape scenarios, but quickly gave up on that thought.

Just as I was wondering how much time I could endure in a place like this before losing my mind, an officer came to my cell and once ordered me to follow him.

We walked down the stairs, but instead of turning to the offices, where I had been interviewed the previous evening, we walked straight out of the front door of the police station.

I hadn't been told anything by anybody and could only assume that I was being moved.

A lorry was parked in front of the station and the officer told me to climb into the back. There were already four other prisoners, including Louis, in the back of the lorry as well as another officer to guard us.

Louis looked at me and nodded, but didn't say anything.

I took the nod as a good sign and hoped that, if not now, eventually, he would be able to forgive me for my costly mistake.

Once I sat down, the lorry shot into motion and we departed for our unknown destination. It was a short ride through town.

Under normal circumstances I would have tried to get a better look at the city, but I was too worried about my future to care much about what Figueras looked like.

After about a ten-minute drive, we arrived at a massive gray prison building right on the outskirts of town.

We were lined up and marched into a hallway that led to a spiral staircase. Since we had officially been booked the previous day at the police station, there were no paperwork stops. We were led up the stairs, after which we took a turn down a dark hallway.

At first sight, this place made the police station look like a palace.

I was expecting the hallway to be lined with small cells, similar to what had been the case at the police station, but there were no little windows in the doors to look through.

Halfway down the hallway, the accompanying officer unlocked an ordinary looking door, which to my surprise gave way to a fairly large room with at least seventy men crammed into it.

The room could have probably fit about 30 people comfortably, but with more than double that, there was barely enough room to move, let along stretch out on the tiled floor and get some sleep. We were shoved inside and the door was closed behind us.

Louis had calmed down a bit by then and had started talking to me again. We tried to stick together, but with barely enough room for one person to sit down, it was next to impossible to find enough room for both of us to sit next to each other.

I tried to find a spot as close to one of the walls as possible so that I could move to a spot against the wall once someone got up.

Some of the people in the room looked horrible. They were skinny and famished, not to mention the smell. All I could do was hope that my stay in this prison would be even shorter than my stay at the police station.

Once I had found a place to sit, I began to ask around to see how long the surrounding men had been there. The fellow next to me was a Jew from Poland. He had been traveling for over a month before he had been captured after crossing the Pyrenees. He had been at the prison for ten days already. The person who had been in there the longest that he knew of had been living in the cell for 14 days. He was hoping that it would soon be his turn to move on, as he didn't think he could handle the living conditions much longer.

Every morning an officer would open the door, shout out a list of names, those men would get up, exit and didn't return. He couldn't tell me where the men were taken to, but he assumed that wherever it was, it couldn't possibly be any worse than the living hell that was life in this crowded oversized cell.

There was no bathroom attached to the cell, just a few buckets at the back of the room, that were emptied out every couple of hours. The back wall had a few small windows towards the top, close to the ceiling, that luckily remained open, which helped to dilute the stench of seventy unwashed bodies mixed with the content of the bathroom buckets.

Around lunchtime the door flung open and two officers brought in a large basket with loaves of bread divided into small chunks. The prisoners tried to form a line, but it's no simple task lining up in a room that is severely overcrowded. It was impossible to see where the line started. Men were pushing each other left and right and it quickly became complete chaos. When it got too chaotic, the guards stopped handing out bread to the person in front of them, and just started throwing the chunks of bread into the crowd. Those who didn't manage to get a piece before the supply ran out were out of luck and would have to wait until the evening for their next chance. It was every man for himself in there.

I was lucky to get a piece the first time they brought food, as the guard just happened to throw a chunk of bread my way. Suddenly it made sense why so many men sat right at the entrance of the room.

At night it was hard to sleep, not just because it was impossible to stretch out, but also because there was a constant chain of noises being echoed off the walls.

There was always someone coughing, snoring or worst of all, having nightmares. Some men would make high-pitched sobbing noises, sounding like vulnerable children during their dreams, while others would suddenly start screaming out loudly.

It was clear that compared to many other men in the room, my journey had been easy. Some had been traveling for weeks, trying to escape prosecution and what would have been a guaranteed death if they hadn't left their homes. Many of these men had lost everything, and would never be able to return to the place they used to call home.

Their screams and sobs throughout the night really put the war into perspective for me.

Few of these men had left home to more or less embark on an adventure as I had. For most men locked up with me, there had been no other option. To run was their only chance at staying alive. Being in their presence, seeing their misery, almost made me feel guilty about voluntarily leaving the security of my home.

Days went by extremely slowly, and as the days passed, despite being able to rest, I could feel my body getting weaker and weaker due to the lack of proper nutrition. The passage of the Pyrenees had taken a more severe toll on my health than I had originally thought. My breathing still hadn't fully recovered and I couldn't seem to get fully rested. I spent most of my time trying to sleep, and engaging in conversations with the men around me, if for nothing else, simply to distract myself from my situation.

On my third day in what I had come to call the "Roman Baths House" for the room's pretty tile floor and high ceilings, I saw one of the most disturbing sights I had ever seen.

I had just finished eating the majority of my afternoon chunk of bread when I heard the distinct noise of someone getting sick towards the back of the room.

I turned around and saw a skinny old man, his shirt hanging loosely from his shoulders, trying to hurry to the waste buckets at the back of the room.

He jumped over resting men two at a time, but didn't manage to make it to the bucket before the entire content of his scarcely filled stomach splattered across the tile floor.

What followed next was an image that will forever be burnt into my memory.

As soon as the man who was getting sick composed himself, two nearby seated men rushed over, started scooping up the vomit and eating it.

I turned away in disgust.

It took everything I had for me not to get sick as well. I hoped that the day would never come where I would be so hungry that I would be capable of doing something like that.

On day seven, my name was finally called. I had never been so happy to hear my name, and to be able to leave a place.

After ten days without bathing, I felt dirtier than I had ever felt before and hoped that a shower would be in my near future.

There were twelve of us who were called to the front that day. Louis wasn't one of them. We had been through so much together since we had departed on our journey across the Pyrenees, and I felt devastated to be separated from him now.

"Leo," he called out as I got up to leave. "I probably would have been caught, regardless."

I smiled, grateful for my friend's forgiveness, and walked out of the cell.

I was led through the hallway and down the stairs without being given any information about where we were going, but I figured that where it was, it couldn't possibly be any worse than life in the Roman Baths House.

Once downstairs, they lined us up and as each of us exited the front door we were handed one last chunk of bread. If I wasn't so hungry I would have thrown the damn thing back at the officer's head, but food, even the three-day-old same chunk of bread that I had been eating for a week straight, was more precious than gold.

There were two trucks parked outside the prison. A group of men that must have come from a similar holding room was climbing in the back of one of the trucks. The officer that accompanied us from our cell ordered us to climb into the other truck. The truck was similar to the one that had brought me from the police station to the prison. Just like on my previous trip, the back of the truck was already full of men by the time I climbed aboard. I remember specifically noticing how much worse the men on this convoy looked compared to the men I had traveled to the prison with. Every single man in the truck looked dirty and malnourished. I hadn't seen my reflection since leaving France, and it dawned on me that I probably looked just as scruffy. At least I didn't have a full beard like many of the other men.

What I would have given to be back in Antwerp, walking the city streets in my freshly pressed suit and shiny shoes, I thought.

Once one more group of men had climbed aboard, the truck shot into motion. We drove for about twenty minutes before we came to a halt. We had arrived at a train station, but were told to stay put. It was a hot day at the end of April, and as time passed, it started to get really warm in the back of the truck. The sun beaming on the canvas tarp above our heads kept the heat in like a greenhouse.

We sat there in silence, most of us still holding on to what was left of our piece of bread. We had learned from experience that our next meal was never guaranteed, and that we should act sparsely with whatever food we did have.

About an hour in, I could tell that the guy sitting next to me wasn't feeling well. He kept huffing and was starting to sweat profusely. It must have been well over thirty degrees centigrade inside the truck. The officer who was guarding us saw that my neighbor was struggling, but he didn't feel the need to step in.

"Give the poor man some water," one of my fellow prisoners finally said when the struggling man's breathing became impossible to ignore.

The guard threatened to beat the man who had spoken up if he dared to open his mouth again, and continued to ignore my neighbor who by this point had lost all color in his face.

A few minutes later, I felt a head hitting my shoulder.

The heat had become too much, and he had fainted. I, too, was starting to feel the impact of the heat and the lack of air.

When a second prisoner visibly started to feel unwell, the guard finally called for another officer to bring us some water.

The water arrived just in time, as I don't think I would have lasted much longer before getting sick myself. I drank a cup of water and splashed some in my face before tending to my neighbor.

I dabbed some water on his forehead with the sleeve of my shirt and tried to pour some water down his throat. After a couple of minutes he woke, coughing profusely.

After three long hours of waiting, the guard finally told us to descend from the truck. I felt dizzy as my feet hit the tarmac road after jumping from the bed of the truck. It took my full concentration to keep my balance and not to fall over.

The guards lined us up and ordered us to march towards the train station where I could see a freight train sitting on the rails.

The station only had two tracks. The second track was empty, but I found it hard to imagine that they would load us into a freight train. Maybe a passenger train was still to arrive, I thought, or maybe the front wagons of the train, blocked from my view by the station, would be passenger wagons.

I was wrong. There were no passenger wagons, and that second train that I was hoping for never arrived. By the time I reached the platform, other prisoners were already mounting the freight wagons. We were being treated as cattle, ordered and pushed into the wagons until there wasn't any more room to fit one more skinny man. The wagons looked like tall, 20-foot long wooden crates with sliding doors. The idea that anyone could force a fellow human being to be transported like this was repulsing. The only good thing was that each side of the wagon had a small window near the roof that let in some light.

I was one of the last men pushed inside the second-to-last wagon. I was lucky to be in one of the last groups to board the train, as the last wagons were slightly less packed than all the other ones. There wasn't enough space to lie down, but we had enough room for every man to comfortably sit. Since the little windows were too high up to look through, there was no point in remaining standing, so almost all of us sat on the floor, looking like a group of nursery school kids waiting for their teacher to read them a story.

With nowhere to escape to, we were left unguarded.

We sat in silence, too exhausted and demoralized to talk, as we waited for the train to depart.

Before long, the synchronized sound of the wheels rushing over the tracks was the only noise we heard for hours on end.

As the time slowly passed, sitting on the floor of the freight train that mile by mile was bringing me closer to my unknown destination, I started to feel scared. It wasn't a panic. Instead, it was a deep fear that was slowly growing inside of me.

Since being arrested, my situation had gotten gradually worse with every move I had been subjected to. Clueless on what was to come next, I could only fear for the worst. Nobody at home knew where I was and without even Louis at my side, I suddenly felt completely alone in the world. Wherever it was that I was going, I had little hope that things were about to get better.

CHAPTER FIVE

Miranda de Ebro

A fter hours of riding through the Spanish countryside, not knowing where we headed, the train finally started to lose speed.

My fellow prisoners and I had been packed in the cattle wagon for the better part of the day.

Throughout the journey, I had been peeking through the cracks in the wooden side panels that made up the wagon walls, trying to get a feel for my surroundings.

For hours on end, every time I looked outside, the landscape looked the same. Rolling hills covered with fields of grain and the occasional field of blooming sunflowers for as far as I could see.

The sunflowers stood tall, side by side, their dark hearts surrounded by yellow petals facing the sun. They swayed gently in the wind created by the passing train as if they were waving us goodbye.

The peaceful view of my surroundings stood in sharp contrast with the way I felt. How could seasons continue to change, spring bringing so much beauty and new life while the entire world was in conflict? It felt surreal.

By the time the train finally pulled into the station, I was so happy to be leaving the wagon that for a split second I stopped worrying about what was to come.

When the wagon doors finally slid open a wave of fresh air came gushing in. I took a deep breath of what felt like the purest air to ever enter my lungs.

The smell inside the wagon, again with only a bucket serving as a makeshift bathroom, had been just as bad as that of our cell in the prison of Figueras.

Once my eyes had adjusted to the daylight, I stepped out onto the platform. A sign in the station informed me I was in the town of Miranda de Ebro, in the Spanish province of Burgos. I had never heard of either one before.

As soon as we had all exited the train, the guards lined us up and ordered us to march.

It felt good to move my legs and walk after standing still for hours on end, but my weakened body quickly started to wonder how much longer my legs would be able to carry me. Luckily, we didn't have to go far. We left the station and walked along the outskirts of the small town. Any locals we passed on our march either turned their looks away from us, looked at us with disgust or shouted unfriendly sounding words at us. There was no sign of compassion.

Not long after leaving the station, a group of buildings clearly built away from the rest of town appeared in the distance. As we marched on, it became clear that this was our destination.

The buildings were set up in a U-shape, the entire area fenced in with barbed wire as a sort of prison camp. As we approached the settlement, I could make out the words *"Campo de Concentration Miranda de Ebro"* above the entryway.

I had heard rumors about the concentration camps in Germany and further east, but didn't know much about them or the atrocities that took place inside of them. Later on, I learned that Miranda was built during the Spanish revolution. Its design followed the German concentration camp model and the camp had Paul Winzer, a German Gestapo and SS member, as the internment supervisor. But at my time of arrival, all I knew was that at first sight, the camp didn't look like an inviting place.

As soon as we entered the campgrounds, we could see prisoners walking around dressed in grey uniforms wearing round caps on their heads marked with the letter P for *prisonero*. It must have been dinner time when we arrived, as we could see the prisoners lining up in two long lines leading to two circular vats. Although we were starving and hadn't had a proper meal in ages, we weren't allowed to join the others. They directed us to a small office building at the entrance of the camp where an officer collected some standard personal information from all the new arrivals. There seemed to be a big emphasis on which country we were originally from. Not that I had any real reason to lie about being from Belgium, but I am glad I told them the truth as it later turned out that our living arrangements were determined by our nationalities, and according to the camp hierarchy one could be a lot worse than Belgian.

Once we had become an official resident of Miranda they led us into the next room where we all received haircuts. Those of us who had grown beards between being arrested and arriving at the camp had those shaven off too. I had never had all my hair shaved off like that before and apart from feeling strangely naked with no hair on my head, the realization that I was likely going to be here for a longer period of time suddenly hit me.

After receiving my new due, they took us to yet another room where they had us strip down. We were given three minutes to shower. After not having showered for so long, the water running over my skin felt divine. It didn't even matter that the water was cold. The thick layer of dirt disappearing down the drain made me feel like a new man. I would have stood under that shower for hours if they would have let me, but all too quickly the water was cut off and I was catapulted back into reality. We were told to put our underwear back on and were each given our own set of grey uniforms we had seen the other prisoners wear when we arrived. I was happy that we got to keep our own shoes. Even though my shoes had definitely seen better days, they were a lot better than what most other prisoners were wearing. Some men had lost one or even both shoes during their travels, or their time in various prisons, and were issued a pair of very uncomfortable looking wooden shoes. Aside from our uniforms, we were also given two blankets, a round metal dish and a spoon. Equipped with our very basic supply package, we were now ready to join the other prisoners. We were ushered out of the building into what looked to be the main courtyard of the camp.

There I stood, in my new pajama-like uniform with my blankets under one arm and my dish and spoon in the other hand. Several prisoners were still finishing up their dinner, but the food line had disappeared, which likely meant that we wouldn't be getting anything to eat until the next morning. My stomach growled unhappily.

All around, prisoners sat talking to each other in little groups. Some were playing cards, and one group was even playing what seemed to be a volleyball match without a net.

Not knowing a single person at the camp, unsure what to do or where to go, I threw my blankets on the ground, sat down and started taking in my environment.

The entire camp was one big rectangle about 200 meters wide by 300 meters long. There were two long rows of ten army style barracks on either side of the center walkway, with the main courtyard located at the front of the camp by the administrative offices that I had just come from. A stone wall topped with barbed wire had been built all the way around the camp. The wall was equipped with a narrow walkway for the guards and observation towers built at 30-meter intervals overlooking the entire camp. If there were a way to escape from this place, it wouldn't be easy to find.

Every group of prisoners that walked by seemed to be speaking a different language. Within the first ten minutes of sitting there I heard Spanish, French, English, Dutch and something that sounded like Russian that I couldn't quite place. After the second set of French speaking men passed by, I decided I had done enough observing for now and told myself to approach the next group of French or Flemish speakers to get some more information on what I should expect from my time here.

Before I had a chance to approach anybody, an older, grey-haired, distinguished-looking man with a mustache started calling out names of several newly arrived prisoners. My name was the final one he called. We were a group of six Belgians, two Flemish and four Walloons. The older gentleman spoke in French, asking us to follow him.

We walked halfway down the line of barracks where he halted in front of Barrack 6, the barrack that housed the majority of the Belgian prisoners.

There, the man introduced himself as Señor Pfefferkorn. He was a German born Jew who had been living in Spain for over 25 years. He was a *kapo* at the camp, a prisoner overseer, who was in charge of showing the new arrivals around the camp and giving them a brief overview of how things worked at Miranda de Ebro. He was also in charge of the barrack that housed the Jewish prisoners which was located diagonally across from ours.

Although he was in charge of that barrack, he didn't live there.

Señor Pfefferkorn was well respected by the Spanish military authorities for his intellectual and linguistic abilities, he spoke Spanish, English, French, Yiddish and German. His respect from the Spaniards earned him the privilege of a private sleeping area by the entrance of the barracks, better blankets and larger food rations.

Standing outside our new home, he explained what our day-to-day life would be like from now on. The day started at 6 a.m. at Miranda when all the prisoners had to report in the courtyard at the entrance of the camp. The mornings comprised of forced labor, which usually finished around lunchtime, after which the prisoners were allowed to rest.

Pfefferkorn pointed to a building at the far end of the camp, showing us where the bathrooms were located. After curfew, he told us, one could only enter the bathroom without pants on, as wearing pants might indicate one was hiding something, or planning an escape, and was seen as suspicious.

The building across from the bathroom was the barrack that housed the ill, including those who suffered from contagious diseases. His advice was to avoid it at all costs, as chances of getting sicker there were higher than getting better. If we did need medical attention, there was an infirmary building at the front of the camp, but that, too, should be avoided for as long as we possibly could, he warned us, since the camp doctor wasn't a real doctor at all, even though other prisoners were. The camp doctor was a Bulgarian guy who had landed the position in some unknown way. He had zero qualifications for it, but as camp doctor he was given double food rations and was allowed to go on frequent trips to Vitoria to purchase medicines. It was thus best to stay healthy during our time at Miranda, Pfefferkorn concluded. He told us the head of our barrack would inform us of anything else we needed to know, then bid us goodbye and good luck. He turned around, walked off and left the six of us standing outside of our new home.

For a second we all just stood there. I'm not sure if we were simply confused by Pfefferkorn's abrupt exit or if we were scared of what we would find when opening the barrack door.

I doubted that it would be worse than the prison we had just come from. At least we had bathrooms here, I thought.

The guy standing next to me, a dark-haired tall guy who was probably in his late 20s, took the initiative. He walked up to the door and flung it open.

The door gave way to a dark open area with bunk beds on both sides of a ten-foot wide walkway. The smell of more than 200 men living in a confined space with limited shower access came gushing through the open door. It was a smell that I was slowly getting accustomed to.

A Flemish voice from inside the barrack called on us, telling us to come inside. Once we had entered we found a short, balding guy in his early forties sitting in a chair at the foot of the first bunk bed.

"Welcome to your new home, guys," he said cheerfully.

He introduced himself as Henri Heffinck. He hailed from the town of Anzegem in the Western Flanders and had been at Miranda for a little over a month. He wasn't the guy in charge of barrack, but the guy who was, was taking a nap a couple of bunks down, so he said he'd show us around.

There was something about him that made me immediately like him. He carried himself with a lot of confidence and there was something to say for the positivity he radiated despite having been stuck here for the past month.

I was assigned a sleeping area on the bottom platform towards the back of the barrack. The platforms were similar to the ones at the Figueras police station, a simple structure made out of wooden planks. With no mattress and not even some straw to soften the sleeping area, we had to use one of our two blankets to lie on while the other one served as a pillow or a cover depending on how cold or hot it was. I was to share my area, which was barely enough room for one person to comfortably lie down, with a young guy who introduced himself as Oskar Lambrecht. It wasn't exactly luxury living, but so far it seemed to be an improvement on the past prisons where I had spent time at. More than anything, it felt nice to be surrounded by fellow countrymen.

Maybe I had spoken too quickly. My first night in the camp was a terrible experience. Once all the men had returned, it became clear that our barrack was packed well over capacity. We must have been almost 300 men living in a barrack that was meant to house a maximum of 200. The thin blanket that I had laid down underneath me barely softened the hardness of the wooden planks I was lying on. I couldn't turn without hitting one of my fellow barrack mates in the back or face and was constantly getting nudged when one of the guys around me tried to move.

It was late April when I arrived at Miranda, and although the days were sunny and warm, the nights were still quite chilly during this time of the year.

And then there were the bugs. This was a new experience for me. I could feel the lice and bedbugs trying to find a way into my uniform, crawling over my skin. Needless to say, I barely got any sleep that night.

At 6 a.m. sharp the camp band started to play, summoning us to the courtyard where we attended what was commonly referred to as *"bandera."*

We had to line up in front of the Spanish flag and were forced to participate in a number of fascist salutes. The morning routine started with the singing of the Spanish national anthem.

We must have sounded horrible, as very few of us actually knew how to speak Spanish. The Eastern Europeans struggled the most, often falling back on just humming along as they couldn't pronounce any of the actual words.

The French-speaking prisoners got a laugh out of switching out lyrics in the hymn with words from well-known French songs. The last line of the anthem, *"Gloria a la patria que supo seguir, sobre el azul del mar el caminar del sol"* which spoke of glory to the fatherland, had been substituted with a sentence from a famous children's song, *"Il y a qu'un cheveu sur la tête de Mathieu"* (There is only one hair on Mathieu's head). It was the only lyric that the prisoners sang with full force and conviction.

After the national anthem, the camp commandant shouted the word "España" three times. After the first *"España"* we all had to shout back *"una"*, one, followed by *"grande"*, grand, and finally *"libre"*, free, after the final calling.

After this, we were dismissed and we returned to our barracks to pick up our metal dishes to stand in line for breakfast.

Breakfast consisted of weak coffee that had the color of rust and tasted like dirty dish water, along with a small piece of bread. It was barely enough to still our hunger, let alone to keep us energized throughout the day.

After breakfast, by 7 a.m., it was time to report for forced labor. We were escorted out of the camp in groups of twenty to a nearby site where we had to move stones from the river to the quarry. We loaded stones into baskets after which two prisoners would each take a handle and haul it to trucks parked nearby, which would then bring them to the train station.

On my first day, I was given my assignment. I was one of the prisoners who had to load the baskets with the stones before they got hauled away, and that remained my assignment for the entire time I was at Miranda. Loading the rocks was heavy work, especially for someone as frail as me, but I was very grateful that I had been assigned this task as opposed to being one of the men who had to haul the heavy baskets to the trucks. Not only wasn't the work not quite as physically demanding, we also seemed to catch less trouble from the guards than the other men who were constantly told to keep going and to speed up. We would work until a quota for the day was reached, or simply until it was time to stop.

Thank god for the Spanish siesta which kept us from staying out there for too long.

During our work we were rarely given any water and if we moved too slowly, a guard would hit us with the butt of his rifle.

Beatings and whippings were common, and prisoners were often thrown in solitary confinement after being punished during work, but the brutalities never reached a point of men being killed on the job.

I worked in silence and tried to stay out of the way of the guards as much as I could.

After finishing our labor assignments for the day, we marched back to the camp where we picked up our metal dishes again and lined up for lunch. After hours of heavy physical labor on just some coffee and bread, it hardly mattered what they served us, as long as we got something in our stomachs.

Lunch was usually some kind of slop of which the ingredients were hard to identify. The majority of the time it seemed to be bean based. It was barely enough to keep us going, and it tasted horrible, but we were all so hungry that we would lick our dishes to make sure none of the slop went to waste.

The only time the food was any better was on Spanish national holidays or on other special occasions, such as Franco's birthday, when we would be fed authentic Spanish dishes like paella. I never would have thought that Franco's birthday would come to mean so much to me.

In the afternoons we were free to relax in the courtyard or to stay in our barracks to rest. The humidity at the camp was hard on my asthma, which in combination with the hard work and the small food rations, lacking any real nutritional value, quickly started taking a toll on me. I lost more weight than I thought I could possibly lose and was weighing less than fifty kilograms just a few weeks after arriving at the camp. Because of my lack of energy, I usually didn't do much in the afternoons.

It was interesting to see how most men stuck to their routines, doing the same thing, with the same group of men every single afternoon.

I quickly learned about the different little groups that made up the camp population.

Some groups were easier to become a part of than others.

There were the career military men who played bridge every day. Evidently, the military group was not one that was easy to join. They spoke and acted as if they had never been arrested, still addressing each other with their military titles, and when possible, ordering their barrack mates around.

Then there were the businessmen. Serious, hard workers who had often been at the center of the resistance in their home countries. These men were usually slightly older than the average prisoner at Miranda and spent most afternoons discussing the more serious things in life. We often referred to them as the camp philosophers.

On the other side of the spectrum were the students, filled with young hope. Dreamers who had left their homes looking for adventure. I fell in this category of age and philosophy-wise, but unlike most of these young men, I didn't have the energy to spend my afternoons working on my physical condition. They would pass time by doing pushups and playing volleyball matches against the Polish guys, an unfair match that the young guys almost always won.

Finally, there were a few smaller cliques. The men who outside the walls of the camp were considered the outcasts of society fell into similar categories inside our barbed wired world.

There were the drunks, God only knew how they managed to get a steady supply of alcohol at Miranda, and the homosexuals. Some would dress up as women and charge serious prices for any form of sexual act. There was one in particular called *"La Hollandaise"* who seemed to be in high demand. I never quite understood why, as standing at 6 '1", with the shoulders of a rugby player and an always present stubble, there was little feminine about her.

Most days I would hang out not far from Barrack 6 and talk with my fellow countrymen. I quickly made several friends. We were all from different places and different walks of life, but enduring life at the camp together created a bond that goes beyond all those differences.

Henri, the guy who had shown me around the barrack when I arrived, became one of my closest friends at Miranda. He was one of the older guys in our barrack and became somewhat of a big brother figure to me. We would sit in the courtyard where he would tell me about the minor acts of resistance he had participated in at home before deciding to make the journey south to join the Free Belgian Forces in England. He seemed fearless, and it was clear that he would do whatever he was able to, to help liberate Belgium from the occupation.

Rene Van Den Rydt, Jean Mauleon, and my bunkmate Oskar also became good friends of mine. Any man who found himself at Miranda had at one point left the certainty and security of home. Back home, most people thought we were crazy, but here, surrounded by like-minded people, we weren't crazy, we were dreamers.

Locked up dreamers, nevertheless.

We spent many afternoons talking about our journeys into Spain, what we would do once we got out of Miranda, and of course our mothers or wives' cooking that we missed so much.

Another popular topic of conversation was possible ways to escape from the camp. We talked about it and talked about it, but the security at Miranda seemed so waterproof that every idea we came up with was almost always immediately shot down. There had been several escape attempts, but nobody had ever succeeded until one day we heard that one of the French prisoners had successfully escaped the camp. Nobody seemed to have a clue as to how he had pulled it off, but the camp guards were livid. During regular times they would already push prisoners around, yelling *"vaya coño,"* an insult that led us to nickname the guards *coños*, but now they would go around beating up prisoners for practically no reason. For weeks following the escape, we had to work extended hours and our food rations were cut, even though we were barely surviving as it was. With all this, the Belgians as a group decided that even if we found an opportunity to escape, it wouldn't be worth it. We knew how much misery it would cause the prisoners who were left behind. We were all in this together and after all, we knew we would be released at some point.

Since Spain was officially neutral territory, we were technically illegally imprisoned and foreign embassies protested these illegal detentions that violated their citizens' international rights.

Early on in the war, the British embassy had started making deals with the Spanish government to release British prisoners held at Miranda in exchange for heavily sought after resources. In 1941, with several European countries having set up a government in exile in London, the British embassy started sending representatives to Miranda to look for foreign volunteers who were willing to enlist in their country's respective military force in the United Kingdom in exchange for their freedom.

Having set out to travel to the U.K. in the first place, and stuck in a concentration camp for the foreseeable future, signing up was an easy decision to make. The first chance I got, which was about three weeks after I had arrived at the camp, I signed up to become part of the Free Belgian Forces in the United Kingdom.

As could be expected, the entire process would take time. The first step was writing to the Belgian embassy in Madrid to demand my release. When there was no record of any accusations against a prisoner and an embassy offered protection, it would issue a prisoner a new passport which would ensure his release from the camp.

Of course, I wasn't the only person requesting a new passport from the embassy in Madrid, and there were serious international negotiations surrounding the value of the prisoners stuck at Miranda. It felt like I waited an eternity just to hear back from the embassy. Once a prisoner received an okay for a new passport, then his documents were sent to the British embassy to issue a one-entry visa for the United Kingdom. All this could take months. Meanwhile, more prisoners arrived at Miranda than were released and conditions kept worsening.

Weeks passed and spring turned into summer as life continued at Miranda. Summers in Miranda de Ebro were extremely hot, which made work a lot tougher, especially since we weren't given any more water than during other times of the year.

The worst part of the summer though was the increase in bugs.

I felt like I was constantly getting bitten. The itching never stopped. Every evening before going to bed I would sit at the end of my bunk, take off my prison uniform to delouse myself, and then put my dirty uniform back on. My days of freshly pressed suits and cologne felt like a lifetime ago, but looking sharp had always been part of my identity and even at Miranda I tried to look as presentable as possible.

My friends would laugh at me for trying to dress up my prison uniform by doing things like adding a scarf made out of strips of fabric. They could laugh all they wanted, at a place that's designed to strip away your humanity, it was my way of staying sane.

The summer heat, combined with the increased stench coming from the bathroom and the barracks, also brought along a swarm of flies. Apart from being annoying, the flies also lead to an increase in dysentery at the camp. It seemed like nobody could escape it.

Although deaths were fairly rare at Miranda, and in comparison to other concentration camps prisoners were treated with relative respect, I did witness several terrible brutalities during my time in the camp.

One of the most disturbing incidents I witnessed was a scene that took place outside the Jewish barrack located across from ours.

After the escape, guards suddenly started doing daily inspections of the barracks. One of the Jewish prisoners, an older gentleman named Mr. Silverman who was in poor health and had difficulty walking, had been found with a bottle of urine by his bedside. When the officers inspecting the barrack figured out what was in Mr. Silverman's flask, they were outraged. His explanation that he had a weak bladder and couldn't make it to the bathroom during the night for some reason only made things worse. The officer ordered Mr. Silverman to pick up the flask and bring it outside. All the other Jewish prisoners were also ordered to join them outside to watch what was about to unfold. It was a Sunday morning, which meant that we didn't have to work, so many of us were just sitting out in the courtyard and quickly noticed that something was about to happen.

I was sitting in front of our barrack, talking to Henri, and had a clear view of the scene. One officer grabbed Mr. Silverman's bottle, dug a little hole in the ground and poured some urine in it. He proceeded to push the prisoner to the ground. Poor Mr. Silverman fell to his knees, too afraid to look up at the guards. Even from twenty feet away I could see that he was trembling.

"Drink it," the guard yelled at the old man, his face filled with anger.

Too afraid to refuse, Mr. Silverman slowly lowered his face to the little puddle. Taking too long for the guard's liking, he kicked the old man in the side.

Now on his hands and knees, Mr. Silverman started licking at the urine filled hole, like a dog drinking out of a bowl.

When finished, the guard replenished the hole and ordered him to lick it up again. This continued, over and over again, until the entire bottle had been emptied. All the while, the officers laughed at him, insulted him and shouted anti-Semitic slurs. They made him finish every single last drop, not stopping even when he lay sick on the ground. When he finally finished they turned their backs, feeling awfully happy with themselves, and walked away. It was a horrible feeling, standing there, watching such a degrading scenario unfold, knowing that if we would have tried to help, it would have only made things worse.

In October, I finally received news from the Belgian embassy. Sadly enough, it wasn't the news that I had been hoping for. Several Belgians had been released since I arrived at Miranda, and I was starting to get inpatient waiting for my turn. In late September, the week of my 19th birthday and my fifth month at the camp, I wrote to the embassy requesting news about my case. On October 10, I was notified that I had mail. The letter read the following:

Sir,

In response to your letter of the 28th, I can only tell you that your liberation has been recommended by our embassy and advise you to be patient until your turn arrives.

Meanwhile, please accept, Sir, my kind regards.
The consul of Great Britain

The excitement that I had felt just minutes prior, before opening the letter, quickly gave way for extreme disappointment. Despite the hard work, terrible living conditions and unknown future, all things considered I had been in relatively good spirits since arriving at the camp. I had met like-minded people with whom I knew I would have lasting friendships, and the idea that some day we would be free, fighting alongside the allied forces, had kept me going, pushing forward day by day.

The letter, with no indication of a timeline for my release, made me feel like my freedom was still lightyears away. For the first time since my arrival, I felt hopeless and even homesick.

Since leaving Belgium in March, I hadn't had any contact with my parents. Even though we were allowed to write letters to relatives, if we had the money to buy postage stamps, I had chosen not to. I was embarrassed about having been captured, and I knew my father would tell me that it was my own fault for leaving. But I also knew that they must be worried about me.

Family members were able to wire prisoners money that they could use at a little store within the camp that sold cigarettes, onions, wine and occasionally some bread. All Belgians received a few pesetas every month from the Belgian Legion that we could use at the shop, but it didn't amount to much, and certainly wasn't enough to make up for the little amount of food that we were receiving. I was skinny when I entered the camp, but by now I wasn't much more than skin and bones, and could really use whatever extra food I could get my hands on.

My discouragement, in addition to my hunger, convinced me that it was time to write to my parents. I bought a sheet of paper, an envelope and enough stamps to get my letter to Belgium, borrowed a pen from a fellow barrack mate and set myself to writing.

I struggled to get my letter started. As I only had one sheet of paper, I didn't have the luxury to mess up and start over. My first draft would have to be my final one. What does one write to their parents after having disappeared months earlier, I pondered. I decided to go with a simple introduction, and stick to some general facts regarding my whereabouts and the situation I found myself in. There was no need to worry them with too many details, and I certainly didn't want to reinforce their idea that I had made a poor decision by leaving. In the final few lines, I included the details on how they could send me some money.

After spending the better part of the afternoon carefully crafting my letter, I sealed the envelope, wrote the address on the front, added the stamps and walked over to the front of the camp where the mailbox was located.

As I stood in front of the mailbox, I suddenly couldn't get myself to deposit the letter. I kept imagining my parents, reading my letter, hearing from me for the first time in over half a year, only now that I needed their help.

Yes, I was hungry all the time, but I was in decent health, and wasn't yet at the point where I couldn't survive with no additional resources.

I convinced myself to wait to post the letter. If things took a turn for the worse, if I got sick, or really got too weak to keep going, I would allow myself to ask my parents for money, but for now, my pride was still too strong.

I went back to the little store and instead bought a postcard. The front image was a watercolor of the camp, painted by one of my fellow prisoners. It showed two men and a dog walking in the courtyard. It looked a lot more cheerful than in reality, but that was probably for the best.

I scribbled a quick note on the back.

"Thousand kisses from your son, Leo."

I added a stamp and walked back to the front of the camp. As I dropped the postcard into the mailbox, I nodded in approval. My parents would soon find out that I was alive and well, but that was it.

When I returned to Barrack 6, I placed my original letter under the blanket that I used as a pillow, and it stayed there for the remainder of my time at Miranda.

Summer was tough, but winter was without a doubt the hardest time at the camp for me. Some parts of Spain have fairly mild temperatures throughout the year, but Miranda de Ebro was not such a place.

Located just across the Pyrenees in the mountainous northwest of Spain, winters were long and often snowy.

We were ill equipped for winter. The barracks barely provided any relief from the cold, and as far as our uniforms concerned, we might as well have been naked. The only good thing about the barracks being overpopulated was that at least we were close to our fellow prisoners at night, getting some extra warmth from our neighbors' body health.

Winter also brought along more food shortages. Without the crops that are available throughout the rest of the year, our food rations were cut even further. We desperately needed more food to make it through to spring. Our hunger had become so bad that one of my fellow countrymen, Pierre Crucifix, decided it was time to do what everyone had been trying to avoid.

We had probably all thought about it before, I know I had, but nobody had wanted to bring it up.

We had a dog at Miranda.

I'm not sure how it had arrived at the camp, but for some reason it stayed with us at the Belgian barrack. It had been there since before I arrived. The dog was very well liked and became somewhat of the mascot of Barrack 6. But when it comes to survival, it didn't matter if it was the nicest dog on the planet. If we got desperate enough, we were still going to eat it.

And so, one November night, the poor dog met its untimely end. Pierre beat the poor animal to death, and that evening we ate dog.

One of my fellow Belgian prisoners had worked at a butcher shop before the war so he was put in charge of butchering the animal and deciding how to, more or less fairly, divide the meat between such a large group of guys. A couple of other men were put in charge of building a small fire at the back of our living quarters, which would be used to cook the meat. Everybody else was tasked with making sure the entire operation went unnoticed to the guards, as well as to the prisoners from the other barracks. Not exactly an easy chore.

The actual cooking part took place during dinnertime, while most men were waiting in line to receive their nightly ration of slop. Fortunately, the men in charge of the fire managed to grill the meat and extinguish the fire before anyone noticed that something out of the ordinary was going on. Once we'd all returned from the regular dinner line, we formed a line inside our barrack and one by one received a piece of dog meat. Each piece wasn't much larger than a couple of bites. I'm not quite sure which part I received and really didn't want to think about it too much. I knew that I needed the nutrients, so I set my feelings aside and bit down on the piece of meat. It tasted strong and was a little chewy, and obviously could have used some seasoning, but I finished every last bit of it. More than anything though, it left me feeling rather sad, so if it was worth it in the end, I'm not sure.

To make things worse, the guards found out that Pierre had been the one who had killed the dog. They decided to punish him by making him stand completely naked at the foot of the Spanish flag near the entrance of the camp for 24 hours straight. When we attended *bandera*, like every other morning, poor Pierre stood up front, facing the entire camp population, shivering out of his skin. He later told us he had never before experienced a cold the way he did during that November night.

Another thing that made winter especially tough for me was my closest friend leaving. In December *Petit Henri*, as we had come to nickname my close friend, received news that his paperwork had all been processed and that he would soon be released.

Over the past nine months we had become very close. Wherever Henri was at Miranda, I usually wasn't far away.

He was a superb storyteller, always telling colorful anecdotes about the things he did to sabotage the German officers stationed in his hometown before he left Belgium.

Although I had initially shown little interest in joining the war effort, I just didn't want much to do with it, and really just wanted to get away from the entire situation when I left Belgium, Henri is the one who convinced me how important it was that every young man who was able should do his utmost to contribute to the fight against the Germans. He came from a simple background, and didn't have much of a formal education, but he was very political and had strong opinions when it came to the war.

He was also great at making everyone laugh, which in a situation like the one we found ourselves in could be lifesaving. It was so easy to get discouraged, depressed and give in to our circumstances at Miranda, that having someone around who could make us all laugh was invaluable. So when the day came that Henri received news that he would soon be free, it hit me hard. Of course I was happy for him, but I also knew who much harder life at Miranda would be without having him around.

On the last day of the year, Henri Heffinck was released from Miranda de Ebro. After *bandera*, as we all prepared for another day of forced labor, he was told to gather his few belongings and report to the office at the entrance. By the time we would return from work, he would be gone. We quickly said our goodbyes.

"Starting the first day of the year in freedom is a promising start to 1942," I told him.

He embraced me and promised me that we would soon be united, and that together we would take down the Third Reich.

After Henri left, time passed slower than ever. It was the midst of winter, and for weeks on end, each cold dark day slowly morphed into the next.

Henri had arrived at Miranda almost exactly a month before I had, so I clung to the hope that the day of my release must be near. But January came and went without any news. By the time the middle of February came around, I started to get inpatient. I had now seen every season in the camp, and pretty soon it would be a full year of living at Miranda. Every week men were being released and even more frequently new prisoners arrived to take their place. The majority of Barrack 6 was filled with different men from those who had been there when I had arrived. Most of my close friends had been released, some men who had arrived after me had even been released. More and more men had been trying to escape occupied territory to Gibraltar or independent Portugal, but the Spanish Civil Guard had also become better at catching evaders at the border. As a result, Miranda was busier than ever. The camp, with its maximum capacity of 1,500, was now housing close to 3,000 prisoners. It was a breeding ground for tension and disease.

On February 20, 307 days after arriving at Miranda, I finally received the news that I had been waiting on for months. All my paperwork had been cleared, and my release had been granted. My release date was set for three days later. I was over the moon about the great news, but nevertheless it was difficult knowing that soon I would be free, sleeping on a real bed, eating real food, while many of my friends would remain in the camp for months to come suffering through each and every day. Saying goodbye to the men who had spent every minute of every day with for months on end was extremely tough. Through our circumstances, we had created a bond that was stronger than any friendship that I had known pre-war. By then, I had been through a multitude of goodbyes at the camp. We always tried to keep it short, and it always ended with the promise that we would see each other again, even though we all knew that we'd probably never see most of our fellow prisoners ever again. My goodbye was no different. On the morning of my release several friends and barrack mates came up to me wishing me all the best for my future, hoping they would soon be joining me in England.

Once everyone had left for daily labor, those of us who would be released that day walked down to the office. We were five Belgians being released. Now that the others had left, it was okay to be openly excited. Walking to the office we couldn't stop talking and laughing. We felt like a group of schoolboys on the last day before summer break.

A representative of the British consulate in Madrid was waiting for us at the commandant's office. Prisoners from other countries who were also being released started trickling in. In the end, we were a group of about 20 to be released. At the office, we filled out some paperwork related to our release and received our new passports.

The clothes we were wearing when we arrived at the camp had disappeared, but the British representative had brought some clothes for us to change in so that we wouldn't have to enter the free world in our pajama looking uniform.

It felt amazing just putting on some fresh, regular clothes for the first time in almost a year.

Less than half an hour after arriving at the office, the long-awaited time had finally arrived. With a broad smile on his face, the British representative announced that we were now officially free men.

"Now, let's get the hell out of here and not waste another minute," he said, patting one of my compatriots on the back.

As soon as we walked out of the camp, our entire group erupted in a loud cheer. We made it. Our time in hell had come to an end, it was hard to believe, but we were finally free. We walked the first couple of kilometers to the center of Miranda de Ebro, where the British representative surprised us by taking us all to lunch at a quaint little restaurant with red-and-white-checkered tablecloths. We must have been quite the sight, a group of scruffy, famished looking men dressed in clothes that didn't quite fit. We ate until we were so stuffed that we couldn't take another bite. It's hard to describe how amazing it tasted, my first regular meal in almost a year. I don't think I ever enjoyed a meal as much as I did that lunch. Freedom sure tasted good.

A group picture of the Belgians prisoners taken at Miranda de Ebro in 1941. Leo is on the back row, with the X above his head.

The author at the concentration camp memorial in Miranda de Ebro.

Leo, (center, bottom row) with fellow prisoners at Miranda de Ebro.

Leonard and Mariette on their wedding day in September 1946.

Leo (far right) in front of the Praio do Sol hotel on the Costa Caparica in 1942.

The author, at the same spot in 2020.

The postcard that Leo sent to his parents from the Miranda de Ebro concentration camp. The watercolor postcard was painted by one of the prisoners at the camp. Leo signed the card "Thousand kisses from your son, Leo"

Part of the outside exhibit in memory of the Miranda de Ebro concentration camp (2020)

Leo (left) and his good friend Henri Heffinck (center) along with another Belgian prisoner at the Miranda de Ebro concentration camp in 1941.

The original copy of the form that Leo signed, agreeing to serve in the Foreign Legion.

CHAPTER SIX

Freedom

fter our lunch the representative of the British embassy took us to the train station, where in sharp contrast to our arrival at the northern Spanish town we boarded a fairly luxurious passenger train.

Looking out of the window, I spotted the same 'Miranda de Ebro, Burgos' sign that I had seen on the day of my arrival. As we pulled out of the station, the letters became smaller and smaller until the words finally became illegible.

A wave of emotions came over me. After almost a year, I was finally free. No more *bandera*, no more hauling around heavy rocks during forced labor, no more bugs crawling all over me, trying to find their way into my clothes, biting into my skinny body.

I couldn't help myself, tears started running down my cheeks. Taking those first steps outside the walls of the *Campo de Concentration de Miranda de Ebro* was the happiest moment of my life. But at the same time, so many unknowns lay ahead of me. What would England be like? Would my role in the Belgian Forces be a dangerous one? Would I be physically fit enough to serve? At least this time I knew where we were going, I told myself.

At the train station, us five Belgian prisoners were separated from the others who were released at the same time as us.

We would be traveling on to San Sebastian, a city on the Bay of Biscay in Spain's Basque Country, to meet up with a fellow countryman. We travelled almost four hours northwest, back toward the French border. San Sebastian wasn't exactly on the way to Madrid, where we knew we would be heading next, as a matter of fact, it was pretty much in the opposite direction, but it was the home of a Belgian by the name of Georges Marquet.

Georges was a big supporter of the liberal party who until 1936 had been a senator in the Belgian parliament. Aside from being very politically involved, he was also a very rich, self-made man who owned several luxury hotels around Europe. His portfolio of hotels included the famous Hotel Negresco on the *Promenade des Anglais* in Nice, as well as the Claridge in Paris.

During the war Marquet was one of just two Belgians in Spain who helped many fellow countrymen after their release from Miranda. He let them stay at his Spanish hotels and paid for their transportation to the British territory of Gibraltar or to neutral Portugal.

Apparently he needed to go to Madrid in a few days' time, so he had decided to have us freshly released Belgians come stay at his hotel in San Sebastian for a couple of days before accompanying us to the Spanish capital.

As we neared the city, the train entered a tunnel taking us through the mountains. San Sebastian appeared from the mountainous territory as an oasis in the desert. The seaside city was protected by mountains all around, giving it the impression of being cut off from the rest of the world.

Georges, who was in his seventies by the time the Second World War broke out, personally welcomed us at the train station before proudly leading us to his Continental Palace Hotel, where we all received our own rooms.

The Continental Palace was a beautiful beachfront hotel that looked like it could have been picked up from the center of Paris and dropped here on this Spanish beach.

It felt strange entering such a luxurious place, just hours after being released from Miranda.

The first thing I did once I got to my room was run a hot bath. I hadn't been able to properly bathe since entering the camp, and although I had become immune to the smell, I must not have been pleasant to be around for anyone who wasn't coming from Miranda. All we'd had at the camp were large concrete tanks filled with stagnant water out in the courtyard that we all used to wash ourselves in. Needless to say, the water was always dirty, and you never had any privacy.

After just a few minutes of scrubbing away layers of dirt, the water in my bath had turned so dark that I decided to empty it and run a second bath, this one the type I could just sit back in and enjoy for a while. It was a feeling of pure bliss.

That evening, even though we were still to prove our value as freedom fighters, we were treated like heroes as we enjoyed what felt like a never-ending feast at the hotel's restaurant *Euskalduna*.

The restaurant, with its enormous windows and high ceilings, already had bottles of wine set out on every single table. Drinking wine with lunch and dinner wasn't just an option in Spain, it was a given.

We celebrated life and freedom until the early hours of the morning. We stuffed ourselves with delicious Spanish dishes such as mussels escabeche, rice with rabbit, and cod, all while downing liters of red wine.

Spain was still very much struggling after its civil war, but there seemed to be no shortage of food and wine at the hotel. For a brief few hours the war that was raging in other parts of Europe, including in our home country, seemed a million miles away.

The next morning I woke to a nasty headache bringing me back to the realities of life. Luckily we had little on the agenda, as we would be spending one more day in San Sebastian before moving on to Madrid. Waking up in a comfortable bed in a beautiful hotel still felt completely surreal.

After taking my time getting out of bed, I decided to take a walk on the beach. February can be quite cold in San Sebastian, and the constant wind coming from the ocean brings a chill at least five degrees colder than the actual temperature, but the sun was out and I figured some fresh air and a quiet walk would do me good. I stepped out from the hotel straight onto the boardwalk.

The bay on which the hotel was located was the most beautiful oceanfront that I had ever seen.

The almost perfect half circle of wide sandy beaches is protected from the Atlantic Ocean by hills covered with trees. At the center of the bay, at the outfall to the ocean, sits a small rocky island in the middle of the water, as if it was placed there specifically to steer outgoing boats to one side and incoming ones to the other.

The sandy beach that separates the city from the ocean is lined with a hundreds-of-meters-long promenade, built several meters above the beach. Two high pillars stand at each side of a central lookout post where people can take in the view. The details on the pillars and the railings along the boardwalk are so beautiful and sophisticated, they look like they belong in a fairytale.

I leaned up against the railing, pausing to take in the view, and imagined what this place would look like in different times.

Children running along the promenade, melting ice cream cones in hand, beachgoers carrying their foldable chairs and umbrellas down to the sand.

The wide beaches reminded me a bit of the coast back at home in Belgium, where when the tide is low hundreds of meters of sand separate the boardwalk from the North Sea.

As I walked towards one of the promenade stairways to go down to the beach, I passed only one other person. A middle-aged man, wearing a traditional Basque beret. He was sitting alone on a bench, passionately playing the accordion. The music was so beautiful that I stopped for a moment to appreciate it. Mesmerized, I could have stood there for hours. It was only the cold that nudged me to keep moving, as the wind engulfed the beautiful sound, carrying each note across the seawall. For the first time in ages, I realized, I felt genuinely happy.

I walked several kilometers on the packed sand to the end of the beach without crossing a single other person. After a year of living as part of a pack, always being around other men, from working together, eating together, sleeping together to hanging out in the courtyard together, it really felt liberating to spend an hour in complete solitude with only the sound of the waves and the wind interrupting the silence.

When I got back to the hotel, I ran into Mr. Marquet in the lobby who told me that the other Belgians had left to go explore the town and have a couple of drinks.

He offered to buy me a cup of coffee, which I happily accepted as my nose had lost its feeling from being out in the cold air.

The brown water that we drank every morning with breakfast at Miranda didn't deserve to be described under the same name as the coffee I drank at the

Continental Palace. The freshly ground beans transformed in a dark, rich roast, unlike anything I had ever tasted before.

I asked Marquet what inspired him to help his fellow countrymen as much as he did. He could have easily waited out the war in his beautiful hotel, sipping his delicious coffee, without ever getting involved in anything.

He paused for a second, looked me in the eyes and said, "I might be a rich man now, Leo, but I come from a simple family of nine children. We didn't have much, but we always had each other. I see that same camaraderie that I had with my siblings in the young men released from Miranda. I'm an old man now and might not be around for much longer, so I want to do as much good as I can with the time I have left. If that means helping a few countrymen coming out of a troublesome time before they head into another tough time, then I'm happy to do so. Plus, I'd give anything to stop the Germans from taking over Europe."

Early the next morning, our entire Belgian delegation took the train to Madrid. The journey took almost all day, but as soon as we arrived in the Spanish capital we were taken to the Belgian embassy. Because it was quite late already, we didn't do much more than be welcomed by the ambassador and were told where we would be staying. The following morning we returned to the embassy to start our interrogation process.

They asked us specific questions about the cities we were from and the streets we lived on to ensure that none of us were spies. Unbeknownst to us, the Belgian embassy, with Portuguese approval, was also doing a pre-screening to help decide who of us would be selected to travel to Lisbon. Later that morning it was announced that both my old bunkmate Oskar and I, along with a few others, would travel to Portugal. They sent some of the other Belgians to Gibraltar, they too would travel on to England or to the Belgian Congo, but would be taking a different route.

The next day was another travel day. It was time to bid farewell to the Belgians who were traveling to Gibraltar as we continued on to Portugal. I wondered if I would ever see them again.

Georges had arranged for a taxi to take us to Curia, a town on the northern outskirts of Coimbra between Porto and Lisbon, where a friend of his owned a hotel. We would stay there for a few days before traveling on to the Portuguese capital.

We thanked our host for his hospitality and said our goodbyes to our former camp mates and were on the road by mid-morning.

The entire cross-country trek from Madrid to the Spanish-Portuguese border was filled with views of the most homogeneous landscape I had ever laid eyes on. For hours and hours we drove through wide-open plains disrupted only by the occasional town or field filled with crops.

We crossed the border into Portugal at Narvao-Beira before heading further west towards Coimbra. Our driver was a quiet young man who understood just enough French to comprehend when we were asking to make a quick stop.

The journey was long and slow, but the four of us who were traveling together were still in high spirits following our release and were excited about the adventure that lay ahead of us.

Arriving at the Curia Palace Hotel, we could barely believe our eyes. It was one of the most beautiful places I had ever been. Georges' hotel had been beautiful and luxurious, but the Curia Palace Hotel was something special.

Although it was located very close to the center of town, the hotel was set on 14 acres of private gardens and parklands.

Entering the property, a hundred meter long center lawn, filled with flowers and foundation, ran from the gate all the way to the front of the hotel.

On the left, there were tennis courts and an Olympic size pool. Behind the hotel were vineyards and vegetable gardens and maze-like paths running through gardens and courtyards with all kinds of flowers and greenery.

The hotel itself was a massive three-story white and grey building with red roof tiles that despite its colossal size was beautifully elegant. The front of the building looked like a crossover between a Belle Époque castle and church. It was magnificent.

Inside the lobby, a late nineteenth century golden elevator cage hauled guests up to their rooms located above.

We spent three days at the Curia Palace Hotel, during which the hotel owner took great care of us. Apart from us Belgians, there were few other guests in the hotel which made our stay even more pleasant. We spent our days walking around the many gardens and simply relaxing, rebuilding some of the strength that we had lost during our time at Miranda.

Every evening ,the kitchen staff would prepare us a lovely dinner using the many fresh vegetables that were available from the garden and some type of gamey meat, duck or rabbit that had been shot earlier in the day. We felt like kings. It's amazing how one can feel like a completely new person after just a few days or sleeping in a good bed and eating proper nutritious food. What a world of difference from the situation we were in just a week prior.

By the time we were ready to leave for Lisbon, I felt like I had the energy to take on life once again.

I arrived in Lisbon on the last day of February, the beginning of six weeks in a place that felt like paradise on earth at the time.

Arriving in the capital city we again went straight to the Belgian embassy on the *Rua San Felix*, a steeply inclining street just a couple blocks away from the Tagus River.

At the embassy we were welcomed warmly by several Belgian representatives.

There were four hotels in the city where Belgian evaders were housed, hotel Pensao Chic, Praia do Sol, Ta Mar and Santo Antonio. Oskar and I were informed that we would be staying at Praia do Sol, a hotel located right by the beach, on the Costa da Caparica, the western coast of the Setúbal Municipality.

We were allowed to settle into our hotel before having to return to the embassy the following morning for our interviews and paperwork.

Our hotel was located on the other side of the Tagus River from the embassy and most of the city, and since there wasn't a bridge connecting both banks, getting to our hotel required a boat trip. Many of these trips across the Tagus took place not on a ferryboat but on one of the many small fishing boats that were always present on the bank. The captains were always willing to give us foreigners a crossing, usually without expecting any compensation. The river was filled with these tiny fishing boats. Local fishermen and women would dock on one of the many sandbars and spend their days bent over at a ninety-degree angle with their rubber booths sinking into the mud searching for clams and small crabs.

We boarded the boat at Belem and were dropped at Trafaria from where we took an old dusty bus to our hotel on the Costa da Caparica.

The hotel itself was nothing special, especially when compared to the Curia Palace, but it was more than we needed. We were each given our own room, with a decent bed and a small bathroom in the hallway.

We were so close to the beach that in the mornings I would wake up to the sound of seagulls screeching as they followed the fishermen back into the harbor. At night I fell asleep to the sound of the waves crashing on to the beach. Both quickly became two of my favorite sounds.

Throughout my time in Portugal, we made many trips between the Caparica coast and Lisbon for further interrogation at the embassy.

Lisbon was known to be an anthill of spies and double agents, which is why we had to be screened and interviewed multiple times by several groups before we could be cleared.

I told my life story over and over so many times that it was starting to feel like I was telling someone else's story, even though it was completely my own.

First, we had to be interviewed by Belgian security, then by the Colonial Selection who decided who all would be sent to the Belgian Congo. (Everyone over the age of forty was automatically sent to Congo.) Finally, the British Intelligence screened applicants who were to be sent to the U.K.

I was happy to find out that I had been selected by British Intelligence to go to England and wouldn't be traveling to Africa. This wasn't a surprise, I had always expected to go to England, but you never know what a selection officer might see or not see in you. Although we had little news from either side of the Free Belgian Forces, what I did know about the *Force Publique*, those fighting in the Belgian Congo, was that they had outdated weapons and equipment, and that tropical diseases such as malaria were raging amongst the troops. It brought back memories of the Foreign Legion recruiter. I was glad that, for the second time now, I avoided being shipped off to Africa.

After we passed the interview process and it had been determined that none of us were spies, we were given a temporary identification card and told to sit tight. We would be notified once an aircraft or boat was available to take us to our next destination.

For the next three weeks we lived a life that was as good as it got in Europe in 1942. Our surroundings gave a feeling of being on vacation. The smell of the ocean, sun-filled days, the sound of boat sirens entering the port, fresh sardines being grilled everywhere you looked. It was blissful.

We didn't have many responsibilities other than a physical exercise program that all the Belgians waiting to be shipped off had to take part in six mornings a week. In total, we were a group of about forty staying at the four different hotels on the Costa Caparica. Monday through Saturday at 7 a.m. we all gathered at a local park for our 90-minute-long training that consisted of a mixture of gymnastics, basic strength exercises and cardio. The runs on the beach were by far the toughest part of our sessions, but all in all the workouts weren't too strenuous and quite fun. It felt good to be doing some physical activity that wasn't hauling rocks, and to be building up some strength again. We also quickly developed a camaraderie amongst the group. Most of us had never spent any time in a conflict zone before, but we felt and acted like us forty Belgians were going to save Europe from its downfall.

After our workout, we were free to spend the rest of the day as we pleased. We spent most days exploring the area, relaxing and sitting on one of the many oceanfront café patios. Depending on the time of day, we would have either a coffee or a glass of wine or beer, or the occasional Medronho, a traditional fruit brandy, in front of us. Every evening, right before sundown, we would help the local fishermen push their large boats, that looked somewhat like a Viking ship without sails, into the water as they departed for their nightly fishing trip, not to return until early the next morning.

Time had passed slower in Portugal than it had in Western Europe. Children ran around dressed in rags with no shoes on their feet, and many of the local fishermen lived in a type of hut on the edge of the ocean. But it was beautiful here, and one couldn't help but feel nostalgic looking out over the mouth of the Tagus River, thinking about the great adventurers of past centuries. This had been the last piece of land explorers such as Vasco da Gama and Christopher Columbus seen before entering vast open oceans on the way to the unknown. Pretty soon, I too, would be continuing my own big adventure. But for as long as it lasted, I enjoyed a break from worrying about the future of Europe and what lay ahead of me, and simply cherished every day I got to spend under the Portuguese sun.

On April 12th, I received word from the Belgian embassy that the next day I would travel to London. It would be me and two other men, Jean and David, whom I had come to know a little over the past few weeks but wasn't particularly close with, who would be making the journey together. We were told that we had to report at the embassy the following evening. but weren't given any further details about our trip. We weren't even told if we would travel by boat or by plane, all we knew was that our eventual destination was London.

On my last night in Portugal, I went out for one final Medronho with my good friend Oskar Lambrecht. We had been together through the hells of Miranda and heavens of the Costa Caparica. He, too, would no doubt soon be traveling to England, but since we were given so little information about what would happen to us once we got to the U.K., we had no idea if or when we would see each other again. Rather than get emotional about our past and future, we decided to enjoy our last evening together, eating sardines and drinking Medronho until long after the sun had set.

The following evening I reported to the Belgian embassy carrying nothing but the small bag of clothes that I had been given upon my release from Miranda. Since I wasn't officially a member of the Belgian Forces just yet, I didn't have a uniform to wear.

Jean, David and I were greeted at the entrance of the embassy by a diplomat who told us to hop into his car, as he would be taking us to the airfield.

That answered my question about whether we would be flying or sailing to our destination, I thought.

I had never been on a plane before and was looking forward to the experience.

The airport was located smack in the middle of the city. We were taken straight to the runway where a plane was waiting for us. The three of us, along with the two pilots, filled up all the seats in the aircraft. Behind us were boxes of supplies. Everything was happening so rapidly, I barely had time to worry.

As soon as we had fastened our seatbelts, the engine revved up, and we started speeding down the runway.

I held my breath as the wheels lifted from the tarmac, the plane narrowly zooming over the historic buildings of the Portuguese capital. Before long, we were flying high above the mouth of the Tagus river, rapidly heading north, at last on our way to England.

CHAPTER SEVEN

England

As the wheels hit the runway, I took a moment to reflect on the momentousness of the occasion. 386 days after leaving my home, I had finally reached my ultimate destination. England. There had definitely been times where I had thought that this day would never come.

The three of us deboarded the plane and were welcomed on the tarmac by an officer of the British Army. We had been traveling a great part of the night, the safest time to fly, and the sun was slowly starting to rise on the horizon.

"Welcome to England, lads. Come along and follow me," he turned around and started walking towards the hangar looking building on the side of the runway.

I wasn't sure what to expect now that we were in the U.K. That, in addition to the fact that I spoke limited English, had me a little nervous.

I was tired from the journey. Although the flight went pretty smoothly, I didn't get much rest. Flying over an entire continent at war isn't exactly the most relaxing first flight experience. I was hoping that we would be taken to wherever we would be staying and allowed to get some rest before getting to the formalities, but it didn't seem like that was an option.

Once inside the hangar we were taken to a small office to meet with the first officer's supervisor. One by one we were taken in and cross-examined. Many of the same questions that by now felt like I had been asked a hundred times over were once again asked of me. Where was I from, which street did I grow up on, how was I able to make it to Portugal? The questions just kept coming. Finally, the officer seemed satisfied and stamped my passport. I looked at it in relief. The oval stamp read "13 APR 1942–Bristol". Now it was official, I thought.

By the time we finally walked out of there, the sun was already high in the sky. It had been at least five hours since we had arrived in England, by now I was both exhausted and starving.

From Bristol, we traveled on to London by train, where we were brought to a sort of guest house in the city where we would be staying, the Belgian Army Hostel at Chester Square in London.

It was nothing fancy, but it wasn't unpleasant either. We were each given a small room, told that we could relax the rest of the day and that someone would come meet us in the morning. It was already late afternoon, and I hadn't slept in well over thirty hours. I decided to take a brief nap before doing some exploring.

After my much needed nap, I stepped out into the streets of London for the first time to try to get a better feel for the city and the country that would presumably be my home for some time to come. London was the biggest city I had ever been to.

Evening was starting to fall as I wandered out to explore the streets of a neighborhood I was told was called Belgravia. The city had been scarred by The Blitz bombing campaign that had pestered London over the previous two years. On my short walk, I passed many buildings damaged by the air raids of 1940 and 1941. I crossed paths with few people on the street, but those who I did encounter walked at a fast pace and only a few of them looked up to make eye contact. Still, my first impression of London was that it was a beautiful city. Not wanting to risk getting lost in the, to me still foreign, city, I kept my walk short and returned to the hostel in time to join the other Belgians for dinner.

A representative of the Free Belgian Forces came to meet us at the hostel the following morning. We were told that for the next few days we would have to attend something called the Royal Patriotic School in Leamington, Warwickshire.

With limited knowledge of English geography I had no idea if that was near or far, but we were instructed to gather our belongings, so I assumed we wouldn't be returning at the end of day.

It bothered me slightly that we weren't given much information, but I also realized that what information was given didn't mean much to me anyway, so I might as well just go along with it without asking too many questions.

We traveled by train to the Royal Patriotic School, where we first received an overview of what the Free Belgian Forces really looked like.

One of the first things they wanted to make sure we understood was that since the Belgian military had surrendered back in 1940 and our constitution specifically forbade Belgians from joining foreign militaries, all members of the Free Belgian Forces were technically committing treason. We had been told this in passing when we initially decided to sign up back in Spain. At the time I hadn't given it much thought, all I really wanted was to get out of Miranda, but the emphasis put on it now reminded me of the seriousness and the potential consequences of what I was getting myself into. If the German's were to win this war, my decision could potentially carry deadly consequences.

The Free Belgian Forces consisted of a newly formed 1st Belgian Infantry Brigade, which included various ground forces who were commonly referred to as the Brigade Piron. The largest number of Belgian fighters fell under this first group. Most of the other Belgian volunteers served in majority British units while some served in the Belgian Independent Parachute Company, which had also just recently been formed. We spent most of our time at the Royal Patriotic School once again being interviewed. This time it was about more than just simple background information. We were asked not just about our time since leaving Belgium, but it seemed like every single aspect of our lives needed to be discussed in great detail. We also went through a series of medical examinations and physical tests. The doctor examining me tried to hide his repulsion, but I could tell that he was shocked at the sight of my legs that were still covered with fresh scars from enduring a year of endless insect bites and the consequential scratching.

I had thought that the interrogation in Lisbon had been thorough, but it was nothing compared to this. It was important for the officials to be absolutely certain that none of us were spies and additionally, they were using the information they gathered on us to determine which unit on the Free Belgian Forces we would best fit in to.

At the end of my time at the Royal Patriotic School I was told that I had passed all security clearance, medical and physical reviews and that I was now officially a member of the Free Belgian Forces.

I started basic training at a place called Malvern a few days later. Malvern was the new headquarters of the Belgian Independent Infantry Brigade.

It felt comforting to be surrounded by fellow countrymen. I spent the next three weeks learning the foundations of how to be a soldier.

Some classes at my boarding school had taught me a bit about the basics of surviving in nature and physical exercise routines, but I was by no means an experienced outdoorsman and had never before handled a firearm.

Still at diminished strength from my time at Miranda, in addition to my asthma, the physical training was extremely tough on me. I was neither very fast nor strong, but what I did have was the willpower to keep going and a mental strength that allowed me to push myself past my limit. I knew I wasn't going to finish first in any of the physical exercises, but there wasn't one cell in my body that would allow me to finish last. While my results might have been less than impressive when it came to the physical tests, I more than made up for it in other aspects. It turned out that I had quite a good shot, but my real strengths appeared when it came time to learn radio transmissions and morse code. Some of my fellow recruits had a really tough time memorizing the alphabet of dots and dashes, but to me it came naturally. While many struggling cadets around me were having a hard time simply getting the radios to properly work to then send off a gibberish of meaningless morse codes, I succeeded with ease. I quickly moved on from correctly being able to wire messages to working on the speed at which I could do so. I also did well on the intelligence testing and psychological review. Although the physical and weapons training was by far the largest portion of basic training, we also had to take both intelligence and personality tests, and had to partake in exercises such as cross examinations to see how we would react to being interrogated in case we were caught behind enemy lines. I did especially well in the cross examinations, always keeping calm and never releasing any of the information I wasn't supposed to release.

Towards the end of my time at Malvern I heard about a request for volunteers to become paratroopers and go to parachute school. I had only recently had my first high altitude experience, but the idea of jumping out of a plane, drifting slowly back down to earth, landing behind enemy lines, thrilled me.

I didn't want to be just like any other soldier in the Brigade Piron, and this seemed like a great opportunity to set myself apart.

Not long after volunteering to jump out of planes, I finished my time at Malvern and was sent to the Ringway Parachute School near Manchester along with the other Belgian volunteers.

I really enjoyed my time at Ringway. Unlike training at Malvern, Ringway was run by the Royal Air Force and instructors seemed to be a little more laid back here. Not to say that training was easy, but there was a fun aspect to it.

Upon arrival at Ringway, we were given a tour of the hangers where we would be spending most of our time during training. We also visited a spacious, almost completely empty room where members of the Women's Auxiliary Air Force, WAARP, packed the parachutes.

The floor was covered with unfolded large, white heaps of parachute canvas, the WAARP ladies sticking out from them like angels amongst the clouds.

We didn't hear a word of what our tour guide was telling us, we were all too mesmerized by the girls.

What a preview of what to expect up there, I thought.

One of the ladies gave us a demonstration on how they managed to fit the huge parachutes into a compact enough package to fit on someone's back. I found it all quite fascinating.

The next morning we started our parachute training. The official motto at Ringway was "Knowledge Dispels Fear." I found it a very appropriate tagline. No matter how exciting the idea of slowly drifting towards earth after jumping out of a plane mid-flight sounded, anyone in their right mind would be lying if they said it didn't scare them at least a little. Add in the fact that we would be doing this in the middle of a war, behind enemy lines, and all of a sudden being a paratrooper sounded a whole lot less glamorous.

There would be many factors that we would need to take into account, which is why our training and being as knowledgeable as possible about the entire process was of utmost importance.

Our training started at ground level. First, we were introduced to pre-jump routines as well as how to fall on landing. All of this took place inside, in one of the hangars. The room was set up with training mats and platforms built up in the air, harnesses and trapezes were suspended from the ceiling, there were even Whitley and Dakota fuselages hanging from the ceiling for a more realistic training tool. The entire setup looked like we were training for some type of strange gymnastics competition. The funky looking setup was the brainchild of Wing Commander J.C. Kilkenny which led to the training hangar's very appropriate nickname of "Kilkenny's Circus."

Once we graduated from inside training, we moved outside but still didn't board an actual plane. The next step in becoming a paratrooper was to conquer "the tower".

The tower was a 100 foot high steel contraption with at the top a sort of crane sticking out over the edge. This apparatus allowed trainees to be launched from the top, suspended in mid-air until they took on the correct landing position, at which point they were released from their cables and floated down to the ground, their parachute safely opened above them. It was the first experience of what floating down to earth really felt like, and also the point where quite a few trainees suddenly decided that they might not be cut out to be a paratrooper after all.

I admit that I, too, was a bit nervous the first time I stood at the platform edge at the top of the tower.

To reach the platform, you had to climb a metal ladder attached to the side of the structure. With each step I climbed, I could feel the unrest in the pit of my stomach growing stronger. By the time I reached the top of the tower, the high altitude breeze adding to my discomfort, I could feel my nerves taking over my body from my stomach all the way down to my toes.

I snuck a peek over the edge. Looking down at the ground far below me, my stomach dropped, and I briefly had to fight the urge to take a step back. Then I heard the command, "Go!" and I knew my only actual option was to jump. Before I knew it I was hanging mid air and in what felt like a blink of an eye later I was back safely on the ground. What an incredible adrenaline rush.

Of course, the tower was nothing compared to what came later that week. After lots of indoor practice drills and several descends from the outdoors training platform as well as a balloon, it was finally time to board a plane and attempt my first real jump.

First, we went and got our parachutes, which were delivered from a chute from a covered hole in the packing room. This way, neither the packer nor the recipient knew who had handled their parachute. The thinking behind this was twofold. First of all, it protected the issuer, if something went wrong with the chute it would have been devastating for her. Secondly, Ringway was a mixed camp, which meant that there was a lot of fraternization going on between the paratrooper trainees and the WAARP ladies, which occasionally resulted in tensions and love triangles and could possibly lead to someone being given a dud.

We departed Ringway on a Whitley aircraft. As was often the case in the field, ten of us would make the descent. We flew over Tatton Park where we jumped in pairs. By the end of our training we would be jumping out five at a time, but for our first jump one man would jump from each side of the hole at the center of the plane before the next duo would scoot up and exit. I was assigned to the third set of trainees. I was glad not to be in the first set, thinking that watching the men ahead of me exit the plane would be reassuring and give me some time to calm my nerves. I was wrong. By the time we made it to our drop point, I was so nervous, I just wanted to get it over with. Watching the men ahead of me two-by-two disappear from the center of the plane was only giving me more time to think about everything that could go wrong. Finally it was my turn, and I swung my legs over the side of the hole. I tried to ignore the butterflies in my stomach and focus on the instructor. The instructor's arm came down as he shouted a loud "Go". I let the rest of my body slide out of the hole and suddenly I was in freefall. My instincts and training took over. Feeling a powerful jolt, I knew that the parachute above me had opened, now I needed to focus on the landing.

I don't think I made the most aesthetically pleasing landing on that first jump, but before I knew it, I was safely back on the ground without any injuries. There was no time to celebrate though, as landing would be just the very start of our mission. Once on the ground, we quickly had to get out of our harnesses, fold up our chutes and make it over to the agreed on meeting spot. Reunited with the others, I took a moment to acknowledge the amazingness of what I had just experienced, then we all jumped into the back of a truck and made our way back to Ringway.

It was at Ringway that I first heard about the SOE, the Special Operations Executive. I met another Belgian at the camp named Andre, who hadn't come from Malvern like the rest of us. He was part of a small training group that consisted of mainly English trainees but also a few international ones from various countries. When I asked him about it, he quickly changed the subject and tried to ignore my question. But I was too intrigued to let it go. Even when he flat out told me that he couldn't tell me anything about his unit, I kept at it. Every single time I saw him, I would ask. It got to a point where he tried to avoid me, but Ringway was simply too small for that.

One morning at breakfast, I once again asked him about his unit. By this point I wasn't expecting him to give me an answer when to my surprise he finally gave in.

"Fine, Sonck," he said, sounding clearly annoyed. "You are driving me crazy, I will tell you, but you have to promise not to tell any of the other Belgians about it."

I eagerly agreed, still surprised that he had finally cracked.

"I am part of a group called the Special Operations Executive," he began. "We are a secret group specialized in espionage, sabotage, and helping resistance groups in occupied areas."

Before he could tell me anything more, I exclaimed that I wanted to be part of it.

"It's not that easy, Leo." he said. "It's a secret army, you can't just volunteer to be part of it, you have to be recruited for it, and then there's a significant screening period and additional training."

"Well, how do you get recruited?"

"Someone who is already in the SOE has to recommend you to the higher ups in London."

I smiled. I knew I had him cornered when he said that.

"Hmm. It sure looks like I already know someone who is in the SOE, doesn't it? Someone who wasn't supposed to tell of the existence of the group, or am I mistaken?"

He sighed. He knew that he didn't have a choice. The second he had given in and told me about the SOE, he had lost all power of negotiation.

"Fine, I will make the recommendation once we leave Ringway. Just know that it doesn't guarantee anything. There are a lot of steps involved in qualifying as an SOE agent, and you should know that is dangerous work. Many SOE agents don't return from their missions."

There was nothing he could have said that could have turned me off the idea of wanting to join the SOE. There was danger in every assignment of every branch of the Free Belgian Forces and beyond. I loved the idea of being part of a secret, specially selected part of the army. Working as a spy, nobody knowing your true identity, being part of secret missions, it all excited me tremendously.

Not long after, I graduated from Ringway and along with the other Belgians who had volunteered to join the new Paratrooper Unit, returned to London. I returned to the Belgian Army Hostel at Chester Square. We were given a few days off and were told to await further instruction.

Andre had left Ringway a few days before me and I was hoping that I would soon be hearing from him regarding my possible admission to the SOE. Meanwhile, I had a few days to relax and explore London a bit more. I spent my days strolling around the city, and in the evening I would usually join some of the other Belgians for dinner. I mostly kept to myself and usually passed on any invitations to go out for drinks in the evening.

It was early summer, and the weather had been favorable throughout my entire leave time. I was truly enjoying exploring this new city while trying to pick up some English along the way. My long, quiet walks also gave me much time to reflect on everything that had happened since I left Belgium.

Secretly, I was dreading the call back from the Belgian Forces and the possibility of having to go into war as a fairly unskilled soldier. Luckily I now had my paratrooper license, but I still didn't feel valuable or skilled enough to no longer think that I was fairly disposable to the army. I also lacked the true patriotism or desire for adventure, I had seen enough adventure over the past year and a half to no longer feel invincible in a way that some other young soldiers did.

I had started this journey with so much excitement, longing for the adventure and the unknown, but deep inside I was exhausted, I felt like I had aged ten years along the way.

On my fourth day after returning from Ringway, Andre came to see me at the army hostel. He was waiting for me in the lobby area when I returned from one of my walks.

"Sonck, let's go for a walk," he said when he saw me walking in.

My feet were worn out from the miles I had already put in that day, but I understood that whatever he wanted to discuss, he did not want to discuss in the hostel lobby. We headed back out and after exchanging a few pleasantries, he cut to the chase.

"I discussed your case with one of my SOE supervisors," he started. "They have plans to ramp up some missions for which they will need officers to deploy to Belgium and France, so they are looking to add some agents. They seemed to like that you speak multiple languages and have already completed parachute training."

"This doesn't mean automatic acceptance," he warned. "But they have agreed to meet with you. I will meet you at the hostel tomorrow at lunch time and will bring you to the SOE headquarters for your meeting."

This news came just at the right time. Something I could look forward to and a possible complete change up of what my role in this war would look like.

I struggled to sleep that night, wondering about how the next day's meeting would unfold, what type of questions they would ask me and what specifically they would be basing their decision on. When I finally fell asleep, I was met with one of my frequently recurring dreams that had been haunting my sleep since my time at Miranda. I awoke drenched in sweat, my skin still tingling from the perceived feeling of hundreds of insects that had been crawling over me in my dream.

Andre met me at noon precisely in the hostel lobby, and together we walked over to SOE headquarters on Baker's Street. On the way over, Andre told me that SOE agents were regularly referred to as the 'Baker Street Irregulars' as a nod to the organization's address as well as its secrecy. Another name sometimes used amongst members was the 'Ministry of Ungentlemanly Warfare,' a name I personally loved.

64 Baker Street was a stylish six-floor building. A storefront occupied the ground floor, the remaining five floors gave the impression of quiet residential flats. Of course, nothing was less true.

We entered the building through a door on the left side of the storefront and climbed the stairs to the fourth floor. There, we entered a standard-looking front door that gave way to a hallway that had been converted into a small waiting room. Andre motioned for me to take a seat while he went up to the young lady working the front desk to announce our arrival. We waited for about five minutes without saying a word, our silence disrupted only by the faint background noise of typewriter keys from multiple machines being punched at an extraordinary speed.

The sound came from a room two doors down the hallway. Its door stood ajar, opened just enough for me to see the toe of a stylish women's shoe. My mind started to form a picture of the leg that shoe was attached to. Shoes like that could only be matched with an equally stylish dress, hugging the frame of what could only be a beautiful young woman. Was she English? Or a foreigner like me? I wondered how she had ended up here, punching typewriter keys at the headquarters of the Special Operations Executive with an intensity that could be felt well beyond the hallway door, punching them like the future of Europe depended on it.

I was pulled back into reality as a slender, greying man in a fine suit appeared at the end of the hallway.

Andre rose from his seat. Without a single word spoken, or even a nod of the head, it was communicated that our meeting was now ready to get started.

I followed Andre down the hallway towards the back office in which the man had already returned.

As I passed the room with the ajar door, I glanced back over my shoulder in the hope of getting a glimpse of the face attached to the shoe.

To my disappointment, the extent of the unveiling was a two-inch heel to match the tip of the shoe. The rest would remain a creation of my imagination.

Once in the SOE officer's office, there was no more time for imagination. The tone of the meeting had been set well before we entered the office, and it was clear that it was a serious one. It was only at that point that I learned that I wasn't being interviewed by just any SOE officer. Sir Charles Hambro was the head of the entire agency! It wasn't customary for someone so high up to meet with new recruits, but prior to leading the agency Sir Hambro had been in charge of overseeing the French, Belgian, German and Dutch section of the SOE which is how he had met my friend Andre. Apparently he liked Belgians. He found us courageous and was impressed with our language skills.

He motioned for us to take a seat across from him. Although he had a quite stern looking face, I could quite quickly tell that he was kinder than he looked. He exchanged a few pleasantries with Andre, then focused on me. My interview lasted no longer than ten minutes, a pleasant change from the multi-hour interviews I had recently been through.

Sir Hambro didn't want my entire background, he knew I had been vetted multiple times and trusted Andre not to bring someone he wasn't one hundred percent sure about, instead he wanted to hear about me as a person. Not the how behind my journey and my decision to leave Belgium, but the why.

He wanted to hear about my skills and about the languages that I spoke, and he wanted to hear about my hopes for the future. About eight minutes into our conversation, he checked his watch and interrupted me mid-sentence.

"I apologize, I have another appointment to get to. It has been nice meeting you, Mr. Sonck. I feel confident in your potential of becoming an SEO agent and will give you the green light to start your training. You will receive a telegram at your residence with further instructions."

An abrupt ending to our meeting, but I got the news that I wanted to hear and that was all that mattered.

I was thrilled. I headed back to the hostel with my head held high. I wished that I could have told all my fellow Belgians at the hostel that I was going to be part of the Special Operations Executive, but of course this was top secret information. I would soon be moving out of the hostel and joining a group of other SOE recruits in a new housing arrangement.

A few days later I received a telegraph with the news that the next day an SOE representative would meet me at the hostel to take me to my new living quarters.

I packed my few belongings and on June 23, 1942, I was officially released from the Belgian Forces and became part of the SOE. I was brought to the SOE Training School (S.T.S. 4), Winterfold House, a 212 acre property about halfway between London and the southern English coast in the Surrey Hills, near the village of Cranleigh.

Winterfold was a late Victorian style country house sitting on enough land for the SOE to go about their new-recruit vetting and training activities without running the risk of being noticed by any unwanted onlookers.

I arrived in the middle of the day when the other recruits were in training. Upon arrival, I was shown my room, which I would be sharing with another agent in training, and then filled out the necessary documentation to complete my transition. One of the documents I was made to sign was an official declaration that read the following:

"I declare that I will never disclose to anyone any information which I have acquired or may at any future time acquire as the result of my connection with this Department, unless such disclosure is necessary for the work for the Department."

The document went on to list specific information in particular, that at all times must be kept confidential such as names, alias descriptions, identities and locations. In conclusion, as a reminder of the severe consequences breaching these rules held, was the following statement:

"I declare moreover that I understand that I am personally responsible for any disclosure of such information I may make and that disciplinary proceedings under the Official Secrets Acts 1911 and 1920, the Treachery Act 1940, or the Defence (General) Regulations 1939 may be taken against me if I at any time or any way contravene the terms of this declaration."

My English might not have been perfect, but I perfectly understood the significance of this document when I signed it, for the first time with my freshly assigned alias, Emile Van Loeven.

As a special agent, even one in training, I received a false identity. From then on, my Leonard Sonck was a name from the past. From hence forward, I would be known as Emile Van Loeven. All my papers, including my Soldiers Service Paybook had my code name on it. Later on that first evening I sat down with a pen and a piece of paper and practiced my new signature, Emile Van Loeven, Emile Van Loeven, I wrote over and over until I was satisfied with the way the curls of my new name flowed out of my pen.

I was told that my SOE training would consist of five stages, if I were to make it through the first stage without getting dismissed, that is. The five stages were Preliminary School, Paramilitary School, Finishing School, Operating Holding School and Speciality School.

The first stage, Preliminary School, would last a month.

At Winterfield, the focus was on basic physical fitness, map reading and firearm handling, as well as psychological evaluations. To make it through all training phases and to be able to call oneself a real SOE agent, one needed to be more than just a skilled soldier. Intelligence, reliability and character all played an important role.

There were twelve men staying at Winterfold when I arrived. It was a varied group, both in age and in nationality. There were a couple of Brits, but most of the men were from the continent. I was the only Belgian when I arrived, though.

I was still quite weak when I arrived at Winterfold and from my new roommate I quickly learned that the traumas from my time at Miranda had made their way into my dreams and were being outed by shouting in my sleep. Probably not the best attribute for an undercover agent.

My roommate seemed friendly enough, but I didn't speak enough English to feel comfortable initiating a conversation with him.

I was excited at having been given the opportunity to become an SOE agent, but my time at Winterfold was tough. The mental and physical exhaustion of the past year weighed heavily on me during training and not having any fellow countrymen in the group made me feel isolated. The introvert in me came out, and I mostly kept to myself unless I was approached by any of the others. That didn't happen in my first few days at the Special Training School, so I started to keep more and more to myself.

The days at Winterfold were long. We typically started the day at sunrise with several hours of physical training that included a long run and obstacle courses filled with rope work, tumbling and crawling. After physical training we got a short break for lunch followed by an afternoon of map reading lessons, weapon handling, psychological tests and interviews.

During the evenings we were usually allowed to relax, however, an SOE agent was never not on the job and this notion had to be instilled in the agency trainees. As such, the organization had sneaky ways of building in tests and exercises in seemingly leisurely circumstances. One of the tests involved seeing how well we held our liquor. No bigger liability than a spy who spills all his secrets after a couple of pints. Thus, one Friday evening, one of the younger, more relatable trainers, invited us to join him for a few beers at the local pub.

"Even secret agents in training deserve to have some fun every now and then, lads," he told us as he ordered his recruits a round of pints.

He had us all fooled as not a single one of us declined the offer. Lucky for me, the training of the past few days had been so strenuous on my body that I decided to call it a night and head back to Winterfold after just one round of drinks.

Some of my fellow trainees weren't quite as smart or as lucky. I found out the following day that two of them had been caught bragging to some local sweethearts about how they were soon going to be dropped across the pond to spy on the enemy.

They never even got as much as a kiss on the cheek from those ladies. Instead, their secret agent dreams came to an early end as they were sent straight back to the School to pack their bags and be gone by morning.

Seeing other men sent packing motivated me to take my time in training even more seriously than I already did. I was determined to prove myself capable of being a successful agent and spent most of my spare time studying the subjects of the day. Playing into my love for looking smart, I relished the opportunity to be able to dress nicely once again and spent hours getting my boots up to the English Army standard.

After a month of training at STS 4, Winterfold House, I was invited to move on to the second part of my training to become a special agent. This next chapter would take place up north, at STS 22, Rhubana Lodge in Inverness-Shire, the Scottish Highlands.

The evening before I left for training in Scotland, I met up with some Belgians in London and went out to dinner at *Chez Rose*, a Belgian pub on Greek Street known for its horse steak and fries.

Chez Rose was considered the social headquarters for Belgians, staying in London during the war. While I was in London, I spent many of my evenings there.

As we were cutting into our juicy steaks, after my time at Miranda I was taking every opportunity I got to eat a good piece of meat, four young ladies in their late teens, early twenties, came walking in past us and sat down at a table at the other side of the pub.

I couldn't tell you one thing about any of the three girls who followed the first young lady, as from the second she entered my vision, she was all I could see. It was clear that she was very young, but she carried herself with a confidence well beyond her years. She was tall, slender, and had great posture. With her chin held high, she walked straight to the empty table across the room, not once glancing around, ignoring the many eyes following her every move. She looked like she could have walked straight off a red carpet into the pub. Maybe it was my imagination, but it felt like the entire place went quiet when she walked in.

Several other men paused and stared as she walked by, but their conversations quickly picked up again. The men at my table kept talking, but I couldn't hear a single word they said. The second I laid eyes on her, she was all I could see.

"Gentlemen, I have to go talk to her," I announced to the rest of my table once I had come back to my senses. The guys looked at me like I was crazy. They had long moved on from the pretty girl who had walked by.

"You don't have a chance," my friend Charles said once he caught on to what I was talking about.

My experience with the ladies was limited, a year in a concentration camp doesn't exactly help a 19-year-old in that department, but just like the young lady, I wasn't lacking any confidence.

I stood up and decisively walked over. When I arrived at their table, the girls were all looking at their menus, so I opened with a comment about the food.

"I would recommend the horse steak, best one in London," I said.

"It's about time we get some service, we've been waiting for almost 15 minutes!" one of the girls said when she looked up and saw me.

I found it hard to believe that she would have honestly thought that I was a server as I was probably the best dressed man in the entire establishment, but her comment still threw me off.

"No, no... I don't work here," I stammered. "I just came over here to say hello to you ladies."

I was annoyed and slightly embarrassed at the same time, I couldn't help myself from thinking that I should have just stayed at my table.

They all stared at me with a blank look. Not quite sure how to recover from this awkward start of our interaction, I looked over at the pretty girl and in the spur of the moment decided to just straight up ask her if I could take her to dinner some time.

"I don't even know your name," she said. "I don't typically go out with complete strangers."

She didn't exactly give off a vibe of being very interested, barely looking up from her menu.

This was going from bad to worse.

In a desperate attempt to save my face, I told her my name and said that everybody is a stranger until you get to know them, all while trying to sound a lot more sure of myself than I was truly feeling.

She seemed to like my response.

She focussed her look on me and took a moment to size me up. Then, she introduced herself as Mariette Loubry and shook my hand.

My friends, who had been trying to follow along from the other side of the pub, could hardly believe that I had actually been successful when I returned to our table and told them that I had managed to secure a date with the most beautiful girl ever to set foot in *Chez Rose*'s. My statement was at least mostly true. My date was still tentative, as I was about to be away in Scotland for the next few weeks. But Mariette had agreed that I could write her letters and that, if all went well, she would go out with me when I returned from training. That sounded like a success to me.

The guys toasted to my courage and jokingly wished me a long and blissful marriage to my Belgian beauty.

I was transferred up to Scotland the next day. It was the end of the summer of 1942. Summer in England had been pleasant. Sure, there had been the occasional rainy days and cool fronts, but the majority of the summer months had been filled with pleasant temperatures and sunny days.

Expecting only a slightly cooler climate in Scotland, I was in for quite a shock. With each mile we traveled north, the landscape seemed to become harsher. Towns and villages filled with country houses, trees and landscaping slowly made way for long stretches of nothingness. Outside the train window, my view of flat green fields slowly transformed into rolling, arid hills where the wind ruled over the land.

Despite the pleasant temperature in the train cabin, simply looking outside made me feel cold. I wondered how anyone could call a place like this home.

My time at Rhubana Lodge was centered around paramilitary training. The basics that we had learned at preliminary school were now turned up a notch.

The Scottish Highlands proved to be the perfect backdrop for this type of training. Not only was it so isolated that the British Army needn't worry about any unwanted onlookers, it was also the perfect milieu to weed out the mediocre recruits from those who truly had everything it took to be a successful agent. It's one thing to go through a few weeks of basic training with the luxury of heading to town for a couple of beers at the end of the day, but being in complete isolation, with nowhere to escape to after a long day of treacherous training in harsh circumstances, was something completely different.

In addition to the previous areas of focus, training at Rhubana Lodge included survival techniques, field craft, demolitions, train tracks and close combat practiced on dummies. It was here that we were taught the crucial skills that were necessary to carry out sabotage actions. Even in training, the explosives and ammunition we used were real, and it was not unheard of for trainees to get severely injured during training. Just as it would be in the field, any mistake during training could have life-threatening consequences.

As I had feared during my train journey to Scotland, my entire stay was defined by cold. Every time I stepped outside, regardless of the time of day, it felt as if the wind blew straight through my clothes and the cold from the ground seemingly magically found its way up into my boots. And then there was the rain. After three weeks, I started to seriously doubt that there was ever an entire day without rain in all of Scotland. It didn't seem to matter how many layers I wore or how hard or softly it rained, by day's end, I always ended up drenched and cold to the bone.

The entire experience brought back unpleasant memories of crossing the Pyrenees. The only relief was the ability to relax by the fireplace for a little while every evening as we returned from a long day of training.

I sent several letters to Mariette, the thought of her warmed me just as much as the fire in front of me. Despite the slow mail service, I also got a letter from her, which made my entire week. She was still willing to go out with me once I returned to England she wrote. After receiving news from her, I longed even more to get out of Scotland as soon as I could.

Any day at Rhubana Lodge was a challenge, but there were several overnight training missions that really took a toll on me. Without any notice, we would be informed to pack our backpacks and get ready for a 24 hr training mission.

We were given a dummy target, a piece of abandoned railroad, or a structure in the woods that the SOE called a 'mystery house' which contained pop-up targets, firecrackers, all kinds of sophisticated training hazards to make the mission feel as real as possible.

Following hand-drawn maps, we hiked for hours through barren landscape, often in the dark, already following a long day of exercises, to reach our dummy target, execute our mission and return to base.

Regardless of how exhausting these training missions were, they did excite me. I could already envision myself, traveling across the Belgian countryside, on my way to meet with contacts about the details of the next sabotage mission.

That was the kind of war experience I wanted to be part of.

I didn't want having been caught crossing the Pyrenees and spending a year in captivity to define my wartime experience. These thoughts encouraged me to push through the misery of training.

Belgian weather might be ugly, but it was nowhere near as horrible as what I was dealing with here, I reminded myself as I hiked on through the never-ending rain, fantasizing of future real-life missions in at least occasionally sunny Belgium.

It was in Scotland that we were taught to kill, not like regular soldiers, but as secret agents. There was no room for bayonets in an agent's arsenal. At the SOE, everything happened quietly and from up close. We practiced close-combat by taking dummies in headlock and stabbing them by knife or hitting them by cosh, and were taught that when presented by a threat, we were to immediately kill without hesitation.

It was drilled into us to:

1. Always fire from a crouch position - never be in an upright position

2. There will be no time to adopt a fancy stance when killing with speed

3. There will be no time to use the sights'

It was also during this part of my training that it became clear that I had a certain level of talent as a wireless telemetry (W/T) operator. The complicated coding and decoding procedures, and the patience it took to send a message, perfectly fit my personality. I had started out reading and sending at 12 words per minute and had apparently improved rapidly enough to be noticed for my skills.

As such, as my time in Scotland finally came to an end, I had shown enough grit and skill to still be considered for a SOE agent position and was sent to speciality school, STS 52, Security Training for Wireless Operators at Thame Park in Oxfordshire.

Out of my entire training cycle, my time at specialist school was by far my favorite phase. The sixteen-week course consisted of specialized radio, cypher, and security training. Not only were our radio usage skills perfected, having to be able to tap out Morse messages between 18-22 words per minute, we also learned how to repair radios and how to use codes and checks to verify transmissions.

Wireless operators played an invaluable part to the SOE organization as being able to communicate important information rapidly could at times mean the difference between life and death. For me, it was my opportunity to play an important role without the risk of my less than stellar health or my mediocre physical strength and condition weighing me down. Here, I could outshine the others.

Although the most important part of a W/T operator's work took place inside a safe house, seated behind a wireless transmitter, this didn't make the job any less dangerous than that of any other SOE agent. On the contrary, the Germans were well aware of how valuable those sequences of dots and stripes, quietly being pinged across the channel from various hiding places across occupied Europe, were. In 1940 already, the Germans had created the Radio Defense Corps or *Funkabwehr*, a vast radio counterintelligence organization with the sole purpose of hunting down radio operators all across Europe.

Apart from the training, which I very much enjoyed, I was also happy to be back in England. Even more so, the city boy in me was ecstatic to be close to London. No more spending my time off staring at the Scottish countryside, instead I got to walk around the city, go out for drinks and food and meet up with some fellow countrymen. And, of course, highest on my list of things I was looking forward to was my date with Mariette. All of it was a much needed change of pace.

Chez Rose would have been the natural place to take Mariette, it's where most Belgians took their dates, and it was the place where I had first seen her. But this wasn't just your everyday girl. From the second I laid eyes on her, I knew she was someone special, and I knew that she wouldn't be easy to impress.

In the letter she had written to me, she had mentioned that she enjoyed playing tennis, so I decided an afternoon of tennis would be a great way to get to know each other a little better. We had agreed that I would pick her up from where she was staying at 2 p.m. I borrowed a bike from another Belgian and biked the few kilometers to her address.

I was so nervous I could barely hold on to my steering wheel. Turning onto her street, I immediately saw her. She was already waiting for me outside her front door. She looked even more stunning than the first time I had seen her. She was wearing a short-sleeved white collared dress with a matching hairband, her tennis racket dangling at her side.

Internally, I felt like a nervous wreck, but as soon I opened my mouth to speak to her, I sounded smooth as could be.

"I hope you brought your A-game Mariette," I opened.

I don't think I impressed her at all, but she hopped on the back of my borrowed bike, and off we went.

I had learned to play tennis when I was in school at *Le Nid d'Aiglon*. I was fairly good at it, too. If I wasn't, I would have never taken her out to play, knowing I would be risking the chance of embarrassing myself. But as good as I thought I was, my skills were nowhere near those of Mariette, who had only started playing when she moved to London in 1940.

Where I was sprinting at full speed and bending myself in strange angles to reach balls, she moved elegantly, making the returns look effortless.

It took a while, but somewhere in the middle of the first set, thanks to one of my goofy looking moves, I was able to force a smile on her pretty face. By the end of the first set, I could tell that she was slowly letting down her guard just a bit.

Between sets we sat down on the white bench at the side of the grass court and took a little break.

At first we talked about everyday things like the weather, the war and how crazy it was to think that on the other side of the Channel men were fighting for their lives yet someone's priority over here was to keep the grass we stood on short enough to play tennis on. Before long, we moved into more personal topics, like how she had escaped Belgium at the beginning of the war.

The second it became clear that Belgium would no longer be able to avoid being sucked up into this mess, her parents had decided to leave. They had lived through the terrors of the Great War and did not want to chance living through something similar again, so they left as soon as they had the opportunity to. The Loubrys were reasonably well off, Mariette's parents worked as tailors, owning their own little shop in Antwerp. But, like most people at the time, they didn't own a car, and their only available form of transportation when leaving the country were two worn bikes, which would have to do to take them safely to unoccupied territory.

Mariette's dad, Paul, rode one bike with his wife, Maria, on the back, while Mariette rode the other bike, carrying her little brother Jean, who was only seven at the time.

With just a few belongings, mainly extra clothes, stowed away on the bicycles and in bags hanging from the handlebars, they traveled to the French border which they crossed as soon as it opened for refugees. They traveled on to Paris, thinking to stay there for a while, but found it closed to refugees, so they traveled on, continuing south down the western side of the country.

By way of Toulouse, they traveled on to Collioure, a small fishing village at the foothills of the Pyrenees on the Mediterranean coast. They had been in Collioure several weeks when France fell to the Germans, leaving them in a difficult position. Just when things were starting to look increasingly hopeless, they heard about a British ship at Port-Vendres that was sailing back to the U.K., departing that very day, that was taking non-French refugees. They rushed to the ship, making it just in time, and departed on a two-week journey to Liverpool. To avoid the risks associated with the heavily mined southern English coast, they traveled all the way around Ireland to finally reach their destination.

Since arriving in the U.K., the family had moved around quite a bit. Mariette's father had enlisted in the Belgian Army and was sent to Wales. Meanwhile, Mariette and her mother had worked in a parachute factory while her little brother was sent off to the countryside to attend school. After several more moves, Mariette was now working for the Red Cross in London.

By the end of our afternoon tennis getaway, there was no doubt in my mind, I really liked this girl.

Not only was Mariette the most beautiful young lady I had ever laid my eyes on, she was also intelligent, witty and had a general air about her that made her look like a movie star.

I don't believe she felt as strongly about me as I did about her, but that wasn't going to stop me. I would offer her anything I had to convince her that life with me would be a path worth walking down.

Of course, war made courtship tough, but the limited number of Belgians staying in England at the time worked to my advantage, not that Mariette's English wasn't strong enough that I didn't need to worry about the seemingly endless amount of young British soldiers parading around London in their perfectly polished boots and striking uniforms. Still, I knew that if I played my cards right, I had a chance.

The four months I spent in Specialist School were without a doubt the happiest of my life. I was steadily advancing through W/T Operator training and being close to London, I was able to see Mariette almost every weekend. With every date we had, she seemed to be warming up to me a little more. I had also made several friends during this time, mostly Belgians, and despite the war, was really starting to enjoy life in England. As such, I was almost sad to end my training at Oxfordshire.

With the last part of my training successfully concluded, I could now officially call myself a Special Operations Executive Agent.

I knew that being able to call myself an agent was a privilege and an honor. I had seen enough men drop out, voluntarily and involuntarily, throughout the training period to realize the magnitude of my achievement. Yet, although I was proud of my new title, I didn't feel much joy. Now came the annoying part of being an SOE agent, the waiting game. The SOE didn't send just any agent to any mission. Each agent was carefully paired to a mission that best fit his or her background and skills, and so it could often be months before a new agent was activated.

Waiting was not something I was used to, or good at. Up until this point, my entire wartime experience had been a non-stop train of events. But now, I suddenly had more time than was good for me to spend on things like thinking about the risks associated with this kind of work.

Slowing down also made me realize how deeply exhausted I truly felt.

As days went on, I started losing my motivation, arriving at a point where I realized that I was not very keen to go on a mission. Every single day, since the day I left Antwerp back in April 1941, I had been living at full speed. From my time on the road, to the toll Miranda took on me, through the past several months of training, I felt like I hadn't stopped for one second. Although the past four months at Specialist School had been slightly slower paced, my training still took the fullest of my concentration and energy and by day's end I always felt worn out.

Physically, I was probably the fittest I had ever been, yet mentally, I felt depleted.

I wanted to tell myself that it would be okay, that I just needed a few days to get out of this funk, but as days went on, I couldn't shake the feeling of wanting to quit.

I felt guilty for even having thoughts like this. The SOE hadn't spent months of training on me just to have me bow out now, but I also knew that I would be a liability to the other men around me if I were to be sent on a mission in my current state of mind. It was widely known within the network that the average lifespan of an SOE agent in the field was about six weeks, but in my current state, I probably wouldn't last longer than a few days.

If I were to quit now, there was an easy way out.

Throughout my training, I had been given access to a certain amount of sensitive data that could potentially be compromising if it fell into the wrong hands. As such, the SOE couldn't just have their failed agents, or agents whose identity had been compromised, on the loose in London or other English cities. Anyone affiliated with the SOE, who had knowledge of a certain amount of information and was no longer able to be of use to the agency, was sent to what was commonly referred to as *the cooler*, several estates in Scotland where these men and women would sit out the remainder of the war without posing a security risk. There was no outside contact for those in the cooler. It was a significant change of pace from being an active agent, but all in all it wasn't a bad situation. At the cooler, your next meal was always guaranteed. You got to live at a nice country estate and sit out the rest of the war in peace. I secretly longed for such levels of tranquility.

For days on end I contemplated going to my SOE advisor to announce that I had decided to throw in the towel and that I no longer wished to be an agent.

I went back and forward between feeling guilty, calling myself a coward and a quitter for even daring to think the way I had been thinking, and wanting to quit so badly that I put on my coat not once, but twice, ready to head over to Horse Guards, to my advisor's office, to announce my desire to be transferred to the cooler.

I was just about driving myself mad when my dear friend Henri Heffinck showed up at the guest house where I was staying.

Henri, who had become an SOE agent himself, had been advancing steadily up the ranks since joining the SOE after being released from Miranda. I had only seen him once since arriving in England as he was frequently away on missions. He was in England for a couple of weeks between assignments and had come to visit his protege and take me out for drinks.

Having seen me at my lowest of lows during our time in Miranda, it didn't take him long to notice that something wasn't quite right with me. We had walked to a nearby pub, speaking few words along the way, and ordered a couple of beers. He waited until our pints arrived to bring it up.

"What's wrong, Sonck?" he asked, getting right to it. "I haven't seen you in months and you've barely said five words since I showed up on your doorstep."

He was right, I considered him my closest friend in the world. Typically I would have been overjoyed to open my door and find him standing there, yet now it did me almost nothing.

"I'm not sure if I was made for this type of work, after all," I confessed. Completely out of character, I opened my heart to my friend and told him all about the feelings that I had been struggling with for the past few weeks. I talked and talked, telling him exactly how I felt, but the second I finished, I looked down at the barely touched glass in front of me, too ashamed to look my friend in the eyes.

What would he think of me? The young boy he had taken under his arm in Miranda had turned out to be a coward. Too weak to go on even one mission.

"Leo," he sighed, his voice not harsh as I had dreaded, but instead warm and comforting as that of a brother.

He spent the next hour talking some sense back into me. He knew exactly how to comfort me. He told me that it was okay that I had been feeling this way and then told me all the things I needed to hear to start regaining my confidence. He told me that my skills were needed in Belgium and that he would talk to our SOE advisors to assure that I would be paired with him on my first mission. He promised me that he would have my back in this chapter of my war story, as he had had my back at Miranda.

Several drinks followed our deep conversation and by the time I walked out of that little pub, I felt like a changed man. I was once again ready to set out and prove myself, to do all I possibly could to make a difference in this war.

I was re-energized after my meeting with Heffinck. I spent the next few weeks, still waiting to receive news on the details of my first mission, keeping my W/T skills and physical shape on point while lying low. Apart from the few people I knew within the SOE, nobody was allowed to know that I was an agent. I wasn't allowed to tell Mariette or any of my family back home. Official rules indicated that I was to keep my employment a secret for 20 years, even after the end of the war. This meant that I had to keep up a false story of my role in the war so that nobody around me would become suspicious. For those who didn't know about my SOE engagement, I was simply a Belgian paratrooper which wasn't entirely a lie.

Weeks passed slowly. Although I didn't fall back into my previous depression of doubts and fears, I was starting to get quite bored. There was only so much W/T training I could do to keep myself busy without it slowly driving me crazy. I was starting to think that I might never get assigned to a foreign mission when one

Tuesday afternoon I arrived at my boarding house after a late morning walk to find a telegram waiting for me.

It was what I had been waiting for so long. I was to report to Baker Street the following day to receive further information on my upcoming assignment.

The next day, bright and early, I made my way over to the SOE headquarters. I was to be dropped over Belgium during the night of December 20th, a week and a half from that day. Heffinck's talk to my advisor must have paid off, as I would be traveling alongside him. Once on the ground in Belgium, our task was to gather information from local resistance groups, wiring any useful information back to England, and would also be participating in a number of sabotage missions. Everything else, we would find out once we arrived in Belgium. All information was on a need-to-know basis and with little advance notice. The more information I had, the riskier it was for both me and the organization. I was told that I could expect to be gone for several months and wasn't allowed to tell anyone about my upcoming departure.

Finally, some movement, some excitement. It all felt very secretive, as could be expected, and I didn't quite know what was awaiting me across the Channel, but with Heffinck by my side, I knew I didn't need to worry.

I spent the next few days enjoying some of the luxuries that London still had to offer that I knew would be out of the question in Belgium.

I took Mariette out for dinner at Chez Rose, where I told her she would likely not hear from me for a while without giving any details on where I was headed. It was common for army officers to disappear for weeks on end during those days, and to my relief she didn't pose any further questions about it.

The following Sunday, it was finally time. I had traveled to RAF Tempsford, the airfield used by the SOE, the previous day. It was possibly the most secretive airfield of the Second World War, home to two special duty squadrons and used solely as a base from which supplies and agents were dropped into Occupied Europe. There, I reunited with Heffinck and was given a little more information about our upcoming mission.

We would be dropped south of Brussels, near Nivelles. It would be the two along with our leader making the jump the following day. For this mission, no containers of supplies were to be dropped along with us. Once on the ground, we were to make contact with the local resistance group, Group NOLA, in Brussels.

Heffinck, who had already traveled to Belgium multiple times, knew who and where to reach our contacts.

We spent most of Sunday looking over maps of our planned landing spot, discussing protocols for what to do if we lost each other, if one or both of us got caught after landing and memorizing the addresses of safe houses. The SOE also made me write several generic letters to my parents that they could send on my behalf, to maintain the impression that I was still safely in England while in fact I would soon be just a couple of hours away from them. It was all starting to feel very real. The day went by quickly and before I knew it, it was time to gear up and make our way to the plane that would bring me back to my home country for the first time in over two-and-a-half years. Soon, I would be home, only now, I wasn't going as Leonard Sonck, but instead as Emile Van Loeven.

CHAPTER EIGHT

SOE Missions

B etween the end of 1942 and the fall of 1944, I made three separate trips to Belgium to take part in sabotage missions. My first trip lasted three months, from December 20, 1942 through March of '43. For the second mission, I spent four months in Belgium between October '43 and the end of February, 1944. Finally, I spent another three months on assignment between June and September of '44.

There was an extensive network of resistance members already on the ground in Belgium, but without much needed resources and intelligence they were limited in what they could achieve. This is where the SOE came in. We were able to bring in equipment and weapons as well as money, which was used to purchase any materials locally available on the black market, as well as to compensate the resistance members for their work. Very few were looking for compensation when joining the resistance, but at the same time any extra money was more than welcome as by the fall of 1943 food available through ration cards alone was barely enough to keep one alive, let alone enough to provide the strength to be carrying out acts of sabotage at night while maintaining discrete regular lives during the day.

When we weren't blowing up railways or destroying documents, we were gathering important information on the ground that was radioed back to the UK.

Despite the constant fear of getting killed or captured, my time on assignment was the most alive I ever felt.

Belgium Dec. 20, 1942 - March 1943

On a cold December night, five days before Christmas of 1942, I was dropped over Belgium for the start of my first mission as an SOE agent. I was dropped alongside and good friend, Henri Heffinck, as well as our leader, a more experienced and slightly older Belgian agent who for this mission went by the code name Caracal.

It was a bumpy flight across the Channel. The turbulence was so strong that I felt happy to be able to jump out of the plane once we reached our landing zone. In hindsight, maybe the turbulence was a blessing, as without it I would have undoubtedly spent the entire flight worrying about getting shot down during my jump.

We were dropped just after midnight. The chosen landing point was situated between Nivelles and Tubize, but we ended up landing 2 km east of Havré and 7 km from Mons.

On top of being off target, I landed in a garden behind a row of houses. Thankfully I wasn't hurt, but my parachute was stuck in a backyard apple tree.

Welcome home, I thought, as I released myself from my chute, dropping half a meter down to the grass.

I was pulling at my parachute, struggling to get the canvas down from the tree while trying to make as little noise as possible, when Heffinck showed up behind me.

"I can't leave you alone for one minute, can I?"

I turned around and found him standing in the middle of the garden, his arms folded across his chest and a big smirk on his face.

"Stop gloating and give me a hand."

Henri had landed in an open field just across from the garden where I had touched down. He had been able to quickly pack up his chute before heading over to help me. When we were drifting down to earth, Henri had been able to keep an eye on me, but we had both lost sight of Caracal.

"Last thing I saw was that he was quite a ways east of us," I said. "It was too dark to tell how far away, though."

It took us two hours, scouting the area in the dark, before we found our leader, and when we finally did, we were in for a bad surprise.

Caracal had been injured during the landing and was unable to walk. We thought about carrying him off the field, but there was no chance of us getting to safety unnoticed. Instead, he asked me to go to the nearby village to look for help.

As Henri took a first look at the extent of his injuries, I hurried back to town.

I knocked on every door I could find, but most remained closed. At the few doors that did open, I still wasn't able to find anyone who was willing to help. The only thing I managed to get was a rusty old wheelbarrow that I found in a farm's courtyard.

I returned to the field to try to assist Caracal into the wheelbarrow and get him off the field in this manner, but as soon as we tried to move him to get him into the wheelbarrow, he cried out in pain.

"This isn't going to work," Henri said. "Even if we get him into the wheelbarrow without anyone hearing or seeing us, we have nowhere to take him. We can't go walking through town with an injured man in a wheelbarrow, it will be light soon."

Desperate, I returned to the village to ask for assistance from one of the farmers who I had previously spoken to.

The farmer, immediately recognizing me from earlier during the night, far from offered to help. Instead, he chased me off his property, pitchfork in hand, yelling that he would help me by calling the police!

I returned to my partners to report on my latest attempt to find help.

We were inching closer to sunrise and it was getting increasingly risky for the three of us to be out in the open field, especially after the encounter with the angry farmer.

Caracal, considering that it was wrong to put Henri and me at risk, ordered us to leave him behind and head for Charleroi, where his brother lived, to ask him for help.

We left our leader around 6 a.m. and headed to Charleroi, which was a good thirty kilometers away. We walked and hitchhiked our way there and went straight to Caracal's brother at the provided address to inform him of the situation.

The brother, who was aware that Caracal had been in England but had no further details, got quite the surprise when we showed up on his doorstep informing him that his brother was back in Belgium and currently found himself severely injured in a field, all by himself, near Havré.

Not quite knowing what to do with the two of us, and extremely concerned about the potential consequences if we were to be seen by anyone, he ordered us to stay at the house while he set out to help his brother. He told his wife to keep a close eye on us and under no circumstances allow us to leave the house.

I didn't want to stay at the house, I wanted to help Caracal, but the brother was adamant about keeping us sheltered and there was no changing his mind.

With nothing else to do, I headed to bed to catch up on some sleep and hoped to wake up to some good news regarding Caracal's situation.

Despite having slept for six hours, the brother had not returned by the time I rose. His wife, who wasn't very talkative, was kind enough to prepare a hot meal for us. It wasn't until I started eating that I realized how hungry I was. It was the first food I had consumed since leaving England almost 24 hours prior.

Back at full energy after my extended nap and hot meal, there was nothing I wanted more than to leave the house and head to Brussels as had been our plan, but the wife wouldn't let us out of her sight.

When she finally went into the other room for a minute, Henri turned to me and in a fast whisper explained his plan to me.

"We can't both just sit here and wait," he said. "I need to head to Brussels to make contact with NOLA. Stay here until you get an update on Caracal, then come meet me in Brussels."

Before I had a chance to dispute his plan, he was already tiptoeing to the door with a finger at his lips, signaling for me to stay quiet.

I couldn't believe that he was leaving me like that, even though I understood that it was a waste of time for the two of us to just sit there and wait for news on Caracal.

Seconds after Henri left, the wife came walking back in and found me standing alone in the middle of the living room.

"He's gone, isn't he?" she asked, sounding agitated.

I nodded.

I was bracing myself for the outburst of anger that was undoubtedly about to follow. But instead, she walked over to her armchair, sat down, picked her knitting back up and shrugged.

"Well, they can't expect me to tie you two down every time I need to use the bathroom."

Relieved, I took a seat in the armchair besides hers. I wouldn't have known what to do with her if she would have been angry. They don't teach you that kind of stuff in SOE training.

The evening came and went, and still Caracal's brother hadn't returned. I was growing increasingly anxious about my leader's whereabouts and the severity of his injuries.

The following morning, the brother reappeared at last. It had taken a lot of effort, but they had been able to get Caracal into a nearby hospital. He promised me that I would be able to go see him the next day.

With few other options, I spent another day in hiding at Caracal's brother's house. I wanted to wire England and let them know of our current status, but I could tell that the brother was too anxious to ever allow me to use the radio in his house, so I decided to wait until the next day, when I would reconvene with Henri in Brussels after visiting Caracal at the hospital.

Caracal was in much worse shape than I had imagined. When we found him in the field, I had realized that he was badly hurt, but the combination of the poor visibility due to dark, and Caracal downplaying his pain, had led me to believe that he would be back up and running in just a few days time.

Seeing him in the hospital, it became clear that his recovery would be quite extensive and that our mission would not be able to be carried out as planned.

After being so hesitant to agree to go on a mission, this was not how I had hoped how my return to Belgium would play out, but there was no time to feel sorry for myself, now that I was here, I had a mission to complete, with or without Caracal.

I went straight from the hospital to Brussels, where I met back up with Henri and a NOLA representative, the local resistance group that was part of *L'Armee Belge,* to brief them on Caracal's accident.

We met at a cafe by the name of *Au coq de Jemappes* in the Haringenstraat, a side street of Brussels' Central Square.

The cafe was a well known meeting place for resistance members, but was also frequently visited by German soldiers who sometimes would literally be sitting on dynamite as the explosives were often hidden under the pub's benches.

The meeting was fruitful. We were able to work out the changes to our plans as a result of Caracal's accident and they found me a place to stay for the next few days where I would be able to contact England to receive new instructions on how to proceed now that we would be missing our leader.

When I reached my contacts in England, they promised to send a new leader to take Caracal's place while he recovered from his injuries. In the meantime, Henri and I were to start gathering supplies while the strategist in the UK reevaluated our original plans to possibly focus our efforts elsewhere now that we had lost precious time as a result of Caracal being out of commission.

I spent the next few weeks gearing up for several sabotage missions that I had received instructions on from England, and also made time to visit Caracal at the hospital several times per week.

Despite the severity of his injuries, it looked like he would make a full recovery. Every time I visited him, he looked a little stronger, and despite his unpleasant situation, remained in high spirits. He hadn't lost his sense of humor, nor had he lost the desire to flirt with the nurses. I took this as a good sign.

I had a close encounter with death, or at the very least captivity, myself, when at the end of January Henri and I were arrested by the Germans when traveling from Charleroi to Hal to meet a contact. When we were leaving the Brussels train station to take a tram to Hal, we were stopped during a routine search by three policemen in street clothes.

We were both carrying a suitcase full of dynamite that was hidden under some potatoes.

I was minding my own business when one of the men walked up to me.

"*Feldgendarme,*" he said, showing me his ID.

He proceeded to ask me to open my luggage.

I prayed that they wouldn't find the explosives, but sure enough, they put their hands under the potatoes and discovered the dynamite. Before I could try to make a run for it, one of the officers punched me in the gut, the other one hit me in the face while the third one took care of Henri.

They then proceeded to search the both of us and took our wallets. Luckily, we had learned in the SOE to always carry two wallets. I had one hidden on the inside of my vest, containing my IDs, and one outside of my vest containing only cash. It was the latter that I handed over to the police.

The *Feldgendarme* threw us in a truck along with several other Belgians who had just been arrested.

I strategically chose a spot at the back of the open truck bed, hoping to find an opportunity to escape. I knew very well that the consequences of being picked up with a suitcase full of dynamite would likely mean execution, so even an escape attempt with significant risk would likely be worth a shot.

For absolute worst-case scenarios, if the Germans were to torture me to try find out secret information, I carried an L-pill. A lethal dose of potassium cyanide captured in an oval capsule the size of a pea. If necessary, I could bite through the rubber covered glass ampoule, releasing the liquid which would stop my heart and lead to brain death in just a matter of minutes. The thought alone made me shiver, but I knew a slow death by torture would be infinitely worse, so I was grateful for the life-ending poison pill that I always carried on me.

About ten minutes into our ride, one of the officers leaned forward to speak to the driver. At the same time, the other officer was fixing his coat.

It was now or never, I thought.

I glanced over to Henri who was clearly thinking the same.

We waited until the truck made a turn and jumped out of the back.

I hit the ground hard, but the adrenaline softened the fall. I jumped up, thankful that I hadn't rolled an ankle or injured a leg during my escape, and started to run as fast as I could. Bullets zoomed by us as the officers had opened fire, but before they had the time to stop and exit the truck, we had already disappeared. I managed to escape with only a mean cut, leaving a bad scar as a reminder of my narrow escape from the Nazis.

When Caracal's replacement arrived, it was finally time for action. I spent the majority of February and March of 1943 assisting in blowing up bridges and railways, and wiring messages back and forth to England.

The sabotage acts that we conducted interfered with the enemy's plans of deporting the Belgium workforce to assist in the German war effort. At the same time, we also lead a propaganda campaign against the deportations in general.

Belgium Oct. 1943 - Feb. 1944

My second trip to Belgium was centered around destroying sensitive documents, lists of names of Belgian men who were to be deported to assist in the German war effort by working in their factories, lists identifying Belgian jews as well as strategic documents.

I was parachuted in on my own, but was lucky to be working with many of the same men I had worked with during my first mission. It was hard to trust anyone during those days, so seeing familiar faces was a big relief.

Heffinck was also back in Belgium and we would once again be working closely together. I hadn't seen my friend in a few months and it felt good to be reunited.

"Glad to see you came back for some more fun, Leo," Heffinck said as he put his arm around me when I walked into the safe house upon my arrival.

He was in the middle of planning a railroad sabotage, explaining the details of the mission to five local resistance members.

I grabbed a chair and listened in on the planning session.

I looked at the men around the table. Most of them were older, as many of the younger men had already been sent off to work in Germany. I wondered about what exactly it was that had led them here. They were all regular men, men who were facing their own share of wartime struggles, trying to feed their families during these tough times. I was amazed at their energy and their devotion, willing to spend their evenings and the little free time they had, risking their lives by taking part in acts of sabotage.

Early on during my second mission, we received information from the Belgian resistance network about a building near Ittre that was being used as an administrative office containing over 40,000 documents related to the future deportation of the local workforce.

We received the all-clear from England to make this our next target.

Along with Henri and two local resistance members, I made several scouting trips to the building.

During one of these trips, in the middle of the night, I kept having a feeling of being followed.

As we approached the building, I told Henri about my hunch and let him know that I was going to fall back to make sure everything was okay.

I quickly found out that, sure enough, we were being spotted by two German officers. Thinking that I hadn't noticed them, they quietly followed us along the building.

I made my way back to Henri and briefed him of the situation.

We told the two local guys to keep moving as we hid behind a wall. One of the officers continued to follow them while the other officer stopped to look for Henri and I.

From the shelter of my hiding place, I pulled out my gun. Remembering my training, I crouched down, took aim and pulled the trigger without hesitation, my shot instantly killing the second officer.

As soon as I fired my shot, Henri quickly ran after the other officer and killed him in the same manner.

Our accomplices, who had been unaware that we were being followed, were quite shook up from their narrow escape.

Leaving the bodies at the scene would certainly result in increased security at the building, something we absolutely wanted to avoid, so as soon as the two men had come to their senses we carried the bodies out of the building, careful not to be seen and disposed of them in the nearby river.

The sound of the bodies plunging into the water took me back to that March night in Antwerp in '41 that forever changed my life. I looked over at the two resistance members alongside me and knew that theirs would from now on never be the same.

Before we had left the building, I was able to take an imprint of the key to the front door to make a duplicate. However, this proved to be useless as the evening we returned to destroy the documents, we found two civilian guards at the building. Because of this, our plan to enter through the front door had to change.

We snuck around the back of the building and fortunately found that two basement windows had been left open. Thankfully, the majority of the documents were located in the two basements, each measuring 8 by 4 meters.

After some discussion, we decided that it was possible to destroy the documents without entering the building, given that they were in separate piles in the basements. Together with my accomplices, I threw gunpowder into the open basement windows and lit the documents on fire by throwing in incendiary bombs.

We managed to achieve complete destruction of the documents, but since the fire had taken place in the basement, the building was not completely destroyed.

During the fall of 1943, morale in occupied Europe was at an all-time low. Food was scarce, the little unfiltered news we received was always negative, and there seemed to be no stopping the Germans on their quest of conquering the world.

Any distraction was much welcomed and appreciated. Any opportunity for a laugh was an absolute rarity and a cherished occasion. As such, Heffinck and I came up with a little plan of our own, one that our superiors in England didn't need to know anything about.

In early November, Henri had come about a three meter wide Belgian flag. No Belgian flags had been allowed to fly after May 18, 1940, when the Germans had taken power.

With the anniversary of the end of the Great War coming up, we knew exactly what to do with the black-yellow-red banner.

During the night of November 10 on November 11, Henri and I ventured out to the Tubize lighthouse. While I stayed at ground level and stood guard, he climbed to the roof of the lighthouse and hoisted the flag. He then placed some soil and a brick between the top of the roof and the platform with the light, in a way that made it look like explosives. As a finishing touch, he wrote "Danger of death, anyone who touches the flag!" on a sign and placed it at the bottom of the flag.

The flag created excitement and happiness all around town, and I am proud to say that it was still flying high by the time we left Belgium.

Returning to England after the conclusion of a mission often wasn't as easy as being parachuted in at the start of one. Every now and then, a plane would land behind enemy lines and hurriedly pick up agents before returning to the U.K., but more commonly agents returned over land.

All three times I traveled back to England, I basically had to redo my initial journey from back in 1941. Only now, I had access to top-notch false identification papers that made travel easier than during my original trip. I was also much more experienced and knowledgeable, but on the flip side, traveling across borders had become a lot more restricted over the past two years, regardless of the documents one might hold.

The first step of the journey back to the UK was to secure a 'line'. The most popular escape routes in 1943 were the Comet Line and the Pat O'Leary Line.

The Comet Line was led by a Belgian 24-year-old woman named Andrée de Jongh. It mainly assisted Allied airmen and soldiers shot down over occupied

Belgium to find their way back to Great Britain. A network of volunteers escorted them south through occupied France into neutral Spain and home via British-controlled Gibraltar. As with all escape routes originating in Belgium, the first stage of the journey went through Paris. From there, the Comet line traveled through the western, occupied, part of France, often including a stop in Bordeaux, to then cross the French-Spanish border at the most south-western point of France, between the French city of Bayonne and the Spanish San Sebastian. From there, the evader or airman would travel to Madrid and finally on to Gibraltar before boarding a plane back to England.

The Pat O'Leary Line traveled on from Paris through Vichy France on the eastern side of the divided country. After Paris, the Pat Line branched off into several different routes, making their way through Vichy France like the routes of a tree.

One route, probably physically the toughest one, traveled through Limoges and Toulouse, then on to cross the Pyrenees at one of the highest parts of the mountain range, on to the Spanish cities of Barcelona, then Madrid and finally Gibraltar. Another common route went through Dijon, Lyon and Marseille, from there on to Perpignan, where some boarded a boat straight to Gibraltar and others traveled on by land crossing the Pyrenees on the coastal side and traveling through Spain until they reached the Rock.

In contrast to my initial journey when I left Belgium back in 1941, for my return trips to England after the conclusion of my missions, I always traveled through the western part of the county. Each time, I was able to secure French false identification papers, which allowed me to travel through Occupied France fairly effortlessly.

Unlike the downed British airmen returning to their homeland, I had the great advantage of speaking French and easily being able to pass as a French citizen when prompted to show my papers.

Despite my initial fears, I loved being part of the SOE and being on assignment. From the second I first landed back in Belgium, I was focussed on our mission. There was no time to overthink things. Yes, the work was dangerous and being caught could have deadly consequences, but the work was addictively exciting.

Mission Francoise - Belgium June 6 - Sept. 1944

My final mission was to be the big one. By mid-44, things were starting to heat up. Now that the Americans were sending large numbers of troops to Europe to reinforce the allies, there were signs of a renewed hope spreading across the continent.

Before leaving England, I was told that my time in Belgium would look a little different this time around. As opposed to the many small sabotage acts that I was used to, we would have one main target. My entire stay, all efforts would be centered on l'*usine d'Havré,* a factory where synthetic gasoline was manufactured. It was our goal to bring an end to the production by blowing the entire place to pieces and thus cutting off the German's crucial supply of gasoline.

I was dropped on Tuesday, June 6, 1944, the day the Allies arrived in Normandy, somewhere near Bievene, southwest of Brussels, at half an hour past midnight.

Again I was slightly off target, landing at the crossing of two roads, between a high power electric line and a telephone line. I quickly detached myself from my parachute and went looking for my partner, Bernard.

After half an hour, I found him, terrified and in low spirits. This was his first mission and it wasn't off to a good start.

Once Bernard had regrouped, we finally disappeared into the night to find the packages that had been dropped alongside us. After three hours of searching, we found the first parachute. Half an hour later, at 4:30 a.m., we found the second one. We quickly hid the material in a bush and headed towards Bievene.

At 5:30 a.m., we finally knocked on the door of a farm occupied by Mr. D. Ghilene. Having expected us hours earlier, he had spent the night terrified, worrying that something had happened to us. He was extremely relieved when he opened the door and found two exhausted paratroopers standing behind it.

We were welcomed kindly, were given something to eat and were able to rest for a little while.

My partner, who had been extremely stressed throughout the adventures of our first night, spent the entire day resting at the farm while I went to Brussels to make contact with NOLA. The farmer was kind enough to lend me a bicycle to make the trip to the capital.

After a good meeting in Brussels, I returned to Bievene that same evening. Now that Bernard had calmed down a little, we set out during the night to recuperate our packages and bring them back to the farm.

Once we had located the parcels, we hurried to unpack them and to our disappointment discovered that, one, all the radios had been destroyed (the parachute probably hadn't opened) and two, my personal package containing my clothes and underwear hadn't been dropped. Instead, it had been replaced with packages of leaflets and propaganda papers.

With the packages safely stored, it was time to start planning for the attack. The following day, after a sleepless night, I left on foot for Tubize, 32 km away. Bernard, who was going to Brussels, accompanied me to Hal, where we parted ways. In Tubize, I stayed with Mr. and Mrs. Boulanger at *152 Deportation Street*, not the most inspiring street name for the time we were living in, I thought.

I stayed there the entire day, mostly resting, before leaving at night for Ittre, about 30 km south of Brussels, to contact fellow SOE agent Louis Chevalier. I spent June 8 in Ittre with Pierre De Lannoy on the Motte farm where I spent most of the day trying to find explosives.

The search turned out fruitful as Louis Chevalier and a certain Charles, whose last name I forget, traveled to Charleroi the following day to collect 160 kg of dynamite at the price of 16,000 francs. A steep price to pay, but if we managed to successfully blow up the factory, it would be worth the cost.

We spent the next few weeks gathering information and developing a plan on how to destroy the factory. Once the details of our plan had been figured out, we made a list of supplies that were needed for our mission.

Apart from the dynamite that we had already secured, there were several other things that would likely have to be dropped from England as they were unable to be found on the black market.

Contact with England was made and a drop date was scheduled for the first week of July. With this being such an important mission, there was no need to negotiate our list of requested supplies, the English were happy to send us everything we asked for, including extra men.

During the night of July 5th it was go time. I headed out to the drop point, a field adjacent to a large forest near Braine le Chateau, along with six of our men. At 1:10 a.m., I noticed the plane coming from the direction of Clabecq.

We turned on our flashlight and gave the agreed on signal.

The plane turned on its lights, circled around us three times and dropped its 12 containers and six parcels along with three men.

Two parachutes carrying containers and one parachute carrying a parcel failed to open. All their content came crashing down to earth and was damaged. Thankfully, the men arrived without a scratch.

As soon as they had landed, I ran over to the paratrooper closest to me to help him with his parachute.

As I approached, the man turned around and to my surprise it Heffinck!

"You didn't think I would let you pull off a big mission like this without me, did you?"

"Here to take credit for my hard work of the past few months, aren't you?" I joked and embraced my friend.

It felt great to have another person on the team who I knew I could one hundred percent trust. Heffinck was slowly becoming a legend in the Belgian resistance. He was known for his courage and quick thinking. We weren't always assigned to the same targets, and when we weren't, I missed him for both his skills and his camaraderie.

My night was made as soon as I saw my friend, but there was no time to catch up, we had plenty of work to do.

At 2:30 a.m., as we were gathering the supplies, one of our men noticed a German vehicle started circling us.. The car had been traveling to Braine le Chateau to pick up some prisoners when its occupants had seen the plane and sounded alarm.

We quickly hid the supplies in the nearby forest and I made the three freshly arrived paratroopers leave with one of our men. They retreated to Mr. De Lannoy's farm where they slept until the early afternoon.

We managed to avoid getting caught by the Germans and quickly resumed our work.

Around 4:15 a.m., as we were still busy collecting the supplies, the Germans returned.

Knowing that we were somewhere in the forest, they surrounded us and opened fire. With bullets zooming around us, I hurried to safety. I was able to leave with two parcels. The other parcels were left behind, we had to get away.

Four of us were able to escape, but one of our men, William Lelieux, a local guy from Braine le Château, got injured and was caught by the Germans. He was taken to Nivelles and later to Brussels for questioning.

In the chaos of the German attack, we had abandoned the 12 containers. It would be dangerous to return for them, but we couldn't risk having the Germans find our supplies. So, the following day, while the forest was still surrounded by the Germans, I returned with Robert Willems, Louis Chevalier and his wife, who stood guard, to bury the containers. Somehow we managed to avoid being seen by the soldiers and succeeded perfectly.

Our victory, however, was short lived, as the very next day forty trucks of German soldiers arrived to search the forest, and with the help of metal detectors they were able to locate the containers.

The soldiers had also started to search the area and later that day, they stopped by De Lannoy's farm where the three paratroopers were hiding in the basement.

The farmer, taken over by fear, suddenly decided to make a run for it at the first sight of the soldiers approaching his property. As the two soldiers were approaching the front door, without much time to think, I quickly pretended to be the farmer and welcomed the Germans into the farm as if it were mine.

"*Womit kann ich Ihnen behilflich sein?*" I addressed them in my best German and asked how I could be of assistance.

They wanted to see the permit for the hunting rifle I was carrying.

Luckily, I was able to show them the requested document.

In an attempt to distract them from the real reason for their visit, I offered them some food, which they happily accepted.

I walked over to the cool box, praying to find something inside.

Nothing would blow my cover like a farmer who doesn't even know the content of his own pantry.

I lifted the lid, mentally thanking that darned deserter of a farmer, as I found a pot of leftover vegetable soup.

De Lannoy's wife must have been a fine cook, as the soldiers seemed very much to enjoy what I managed to put on the table for them.

I stood to the side, trying to look as relaxed as possible, desperately hoping the paratroopers below in the basement stayed quiet, as the Germans scarfed down every last drop of soup. The food relaxed the officers and they didn't seem too suspicious of me.

After they ate I showed them around the farm, avoiding any area remotely close to the basement entrance. Satisfied with their rather superficial search, not having found anything wrong, they thanked me for the meal and left.

As soon as I closed the front door behind them, I let out a deep sigh of relief. I had been lucky and I knew it.

That same afternoon I relocated the paratroopers, hiding two with Mr. Lejeune in Ittre and the other one at Jean Dumont's farm in Baudemont.

Those soldiers might not have carried out a thorough search, but there was no guarantee a different set of soldiers wouldn't be returning later on.

Early the next morning I traveled to Brussels to report the recent events to NOLA. They instructed me to do my all to avoid the remainder of supplies falling in German hands. This proved to be quite the challenge as the next day the Germans found the 21 parachutes that we had buried. For some reason, they decided to blow up the hideaway using dynamite.

Since the drop, I had spent every moment I could non-stop circling the forest, disguised and accompanied by a dog. Without what was left of the supplies, our entire mission was at risk.

I observed the Germans' behavior while trying to save what was left of our materials. The soldiers stopped me multiple times. Each time, I showed them my documentation papers and a park ranger identification card that I had been able to secure, which seemed to satisfy their concerns about me.

After five days, the Germans were still in the forest. But then, finally, we got a lucky break. Around noon on July 10, some allied paratroopers dropped just north of Tubize, which resulted in the Germans leaving to assess the situation over there.

I took advantage of their temporary departure to go recuperate the remaining six parcels that were still buried in the forest. I was able to gather the materials and left it at Mr. Hubert in the company of Louis Chevalier and Robert Willems.

I was finally starting to unwind after a stressful week, when in the late afternoon, I got stopped by some German soldiers in Ittre when crossing the bridge over the rail road

"*Feldgendarme*, identification papers, please."

Not again, I thought.

From the start, it was clear that these soldiers were out to bother people.

They held me for 15 minutes. Despite presenting an identity card that showed my affiliation to the Red Cross, they tried to intimidate me by acting as if they had just caught the chief of the Belgian Army. I knew that looking too confident would annoy them and likely result in further searches or even an arrest, so instead I played up my fear, apologizing over and over and repeating that I had nothing to do with the Belgian Army, that I was just a simple Red Cross volunteer. They were enjoying my misery. I was starting to get a bit concerned when, finally, they let me go.

Without the full list of supplies that we had requested, it was impossible for us to move forward with the destruction of the factory. Along with the team, I spent the next two weeks reorganizing and meeting with many of my contacts to facilitate a second material drop after only having been able to recuperate a small portion of the needed supplies.

Between finding a new location to drop the supplies, far enough from any main roads and at low risk of being discovered by any nearby stationed Germans, and several of our men being picked up by the enemy, I had my work cut out for me.

Finally, during the night of July 31, the drop was able to take place in Roisin. Twelve containers of supplies, four parcels containing explosives and weapons were all safely received that night.

Meanwhile, NOLA had been working on providing us with human reinforcement. The allied forces had been making significant headway at the front, which encouraged numerous men who had previously been too cautious to take on a significant role in the resistance to finally step up.

The next day, forty police officers, recruited by NOLA, volunteered to assist in our mission. They brought along with them several cars, two trucks and two motor sidecars.

With the unexpected delays, and with things heating up at the front, we decided that simply blowing up the factory wouldn't be enough. This might be our final big attack, and we were going to make it count.

It was decided that on the same night as the factory explosion, we would attack several other targets in the area. This should keep the Germans busy for days, and would impact their logistics for weeks.

Despite our growing list of volunteers, we were still well below target numbers. By the afternoon of August 3, we had 76 men as opposed to the 200-300 we had hoped for. But, there was no more time to waste, we had to get started.

There were twelve SOE agents working on *Mission Francoise*, as our mission was called. Each of us was responsible for a different part of the attacks that would take place during the night of August 5th. Each agent had a group of civilian resistance members working under him.

If everything went according to plan, this would be the largest coordinated series of attacks of the Belgian resistance network since the beginning of the war.

As I had known from the moment I arrived in Belgium, I had been assigned to the group responsible for destroying the factory in Ittre. Because this was by far our largest target, there were two other SOE agents on my team as well as twenty civilians.

We had men working inside the plant who had provided us with the blue prints of the factory, we had secured enough dynamite to blow the place to pieces and had finally received the remainder of necessary supplies to set our plan into motion.

We had been fine-tuning the plan for weeks now, since my arrival back in June, and if we didn't act soon, our window of opportunity might close.

During the night of August 4, along with five volunteers, I set out to the factory for a final scouting mission.

After the sun had set, the six of us headed out in a small convoy. I was riding in the motor sidecar up front, followed by a car with our remaining four men.

We were quietly making our way towards the factory, with only the moon lighting up the road in front of us, when suddenly we came face to face with a German patrol unit.

It was past curfew so it was to be expected that they would stop us to check our papers, but instead, they immediately opened fire.

Before we could react, the German officers started to unload their machine guns on us.

I was no further than twelve meters removed from the enemy when bullets started zooming by me. As if by a miracle, I didn't get shot.

As soon as I had a chance to regroup, I started firing back at them.

I jumped out of the sidecar and ran to the shelter of the bushes on the side of the road. Thankfully, I had a couple of grenades on me.

I threw a grenade towards the German army vehicle and ducked down for cover. The explosion shook the ground under my feet, and for a few seconds all sound stopped. For a brief moment, I thought it was all over, but almost immediately the shooting recommenced.

I had one more grenade left. I knew I had to use it wisely.

From the cover of the bushes, I tried to get a grasp on the situation.

One of our men was using the second vehicle for cover, but I couldn't locate the other two. From what I could see, there were at least six German soldiers. If I didn't act now, it would only be a matter of time before the Germans took control. There was no time to wait.

I flung the second grenade as far as I could in the direction of the officers.

As soon as the grenade exploded, I blew my whistle, giving our men the signal to retreat.

With no time to get to the vehicles, which were by now badly shot up anyway, I ran about a kilometer back in the direction from where we had come. There I waited for the others.

After what felt like the longest couple of minutes of my life, two of them appeared.

One had his arm around the other's shoulder, supporting him as they made their way towards me. As they got closer, it became clear that a bullet had hit him in the side, above his left hip.

"What about the others?" I asked as soon as they were within hearing distance.

The uninjured man simply shook his head.

My heart sank, but now was not the time to grieve. We hurried back to mission headquarters as fast as the injured man allowed us to.

We entered the mission base, the injured man between us and a trail of blood droplets behind us.

Four men who were sitting around a table going over plans came rushing towards us.

"What happened?" they all exclaimed simultaneously, as soon as we walked in.

I briefly explained what had occurred, while one of the men tended to the wounded fellow.

"We have to proceed with the plan tonight," I said once the others were caught up.

"Now that the Germans know that we are planning something, we can't afford to wait until tomorrow. They'll have the whole area brimming with officers if we wait any longer. Months of planning could go to waste."

We all agreed that it was impossible to pull off the mission a day early at the scale that we had planned. Most of our agents and volunteers had left for the night and it would be unsafe to rush the inexperienced local resistance members into action.

We had to focus on the main target, the factory.

I looked around the warehouse that served as our headquarters. Over the past few weeks, we had gradually moved all of our supplies here. The space was filled with several vehicles and lots of weapons and ammunition. Apart from the four men sitting around the table, I counted another five men standing around the room. Most of them were experienced SOE agents, including Heffinck. That meant that, counting out the injured fellow and someone who would have to stay with him, we had a crew of eight available men to take care of blowing up the factory.

This was four less than we had planned. The original scheme called for eight men to place the dynamite at four locations around the plant, while four men stood guard at several spots just outside of the fence line.

"The dynamite is too heavy for just one person to carry," one of the agents remarked.

"Yes, but we'll need men on the lookout."

We went back and forward for a while, trying to come up with the most effective solution. With the factory floor plans spread out on the table, we gathered around.

We settled on three explosions instead of four, and just two men to keep an eye on things.

"I don't think we'll be able to achieve full destruction with just three explosions," I remarked.

"Then we'll have to position the dynamite where we can do the most damage."

With all eight of us bent over the floor plans, we agreed to leave out the explosion planned for the north side of the factory, located closest to the main entry. The most crucial targets were the south and west side, where the majority of the manufacturing took place.

Our two men on the lookout would stay about half a kilometer back, patrolling between the three spots. If danger loomed, they would blow a sharp whistle, warning us of the treat.

I glanced at my watch, it was almost 1 a.m. and time for us to get going.

We loaded six boxes of dynamite into the back of one of the trucks the police officers had given us. The marked police truck allowed us to move about more freely, but still we'd have to be careful not to run into any German convoys, especially after what happened earlier in the evening.

We added enough weapons and ammunition, just in case we'd have to fight ourselves out of another showdown, then all piled into the truck and headed out.

Sitting in the back of the truck, I couldn't see anything of what was happening outside. I tightened my grip around the rifle I was holding. I was terrified that, any moment now, the truck would come to a screeching halt and the shooting would recommence.

"You okay, Van Loeven?" The guy next to me asked, giving me a concerned look.

I nodded.

The factory was only a short drive away, but the ride felt like it took an eternity.

At last, the truck stopped, and the driver came around to let us out of the back.

So far, so good, I thought.

Moving as quickly as we could, my partner Tom and I unloaded two boxes of dynamite and started moving toward the fence. We were responsible for the west side of the factory. Once we reached the fence, we used wire cutters to create a hole large enough for a man to crawl through.

Tom crawled through the hole, I then handed him the boxes of dynamite before joining him on the other side of the fence. Cautious not to lose too much time, we quickly covered the hole in the hope that it wouldn't be noticeable to any patrolling officers.

Based on the blue prints, the target for our explosion was one hundred paces to the west.

The boxes of dynamite between us, Tom and I counted out our steps until we reached the exact spot.

On the outside of the building, the spot we had chosen looked just like any other spot along the wall. We had to trust that we had correctly used the blue prints, and that this was indeed the best place for the explosion.

While Tom was looking out for patrols, I went to work on setting up the explosives.

To detonate the dynamite from a safe distance, I had to turn the explosives into a time-bomb by attaching a timer.

I carefully laid out the dynamite before grabbing the necessary wires and timer out of my backpack.

This was the most sophisticated, and largest, time-bomb I'd ever made. I knew that even the smallest error could have deadly consequences.

Going back to my SOE training, I tried to calm my nerves and focused on making my way through each step of the process.

"How's it going? Are you almost finished?"

Tom was constantly looking over his shoulder, seeing how I was getting on.

"Just make sure there's no one coming, Tom. Let me focus."

I took a deep breath and carefully attached the wire from the timer to the explosives, the most dangerous part of the assembly.

After I double-checked my work, I set the timer to ten minutes and told Tom that we were good to go.

"Let's hope this will work."

Crouched down, we cautiously ran back to the hole in the fence.

Just as Tom was climbing through the hole behind me, two back-to-back gunshots broke the silence of the night.

We glanced at each other and started sprinting towards the truck.

Arriving at the vehicle, we found the driver dragging one of two dead bodies into the cover of a bush.

He looked at me with wide eyes, unsure of what to say.

"Leave him," I said. "We need to get out of here."

Two of our men who had set up one of the other bombs came running up.

"The others are struggling with their set up, they told us to go ahead. They'll find their own way back."

Heffick was one of the two men still setting up that final bomb. I knew my friend, there was no way that he would walk away before the setup was complete, even if that meant risking getting caught up in the other two explosions.

As we jumped in the truck, I hoped and prayed that Heffinck would manage to complete his setup before the other two timers went off.

I had crawled in the back, along with five other men. We sat in silence as the truck started its way back. We were all dealing with the emotions and stress of the past hour, too tense to talk.

Two minutes into our drive, a large bang cut the silence. The first explosion.

Without missing a beat, the truck continued on.

Twenty seconds later, a second explosion echoed through the night.

Still, we remained silent. We were all waiting, hoping for that final explosion.

I silently counted the seconds as the pause grew longer. 36, 37, 38. I became increasingly worried with each second that passed by. 42, 43, 44.

Then, finally, bang!

The third bomb exploded.

I looked up at the men around me. One by one, they started to smile. Then one man erupted into laughter, and we all followed suit. Our emotions came gushing out in the form of laughter. If you didn't know any better, you would have thought that we were all drunk.

By the time we made it back to the warehouse, we had composed ourselves.

We were still smiling when the driver flung the back of the truck open.

"We did it, guys!"

We jumped out of the truck as hugs and handshakes filled the room.

The mission had been a success, but a small piece of me was holding back on the excitement. Although the third bomb had exploded, until the men arrived, there was no way of telling if Heffinck and his partner had been able to get away safely.

The two men had ninety minutes to make it to the safe house before we'd have to move on without them. It wouldn't be safe for us to stay in the area much longer.

As we waited for our fellow resistance members, we started a small celebration. I joined the men in a toast, but I was too worried about Heffinck to fully enjoy the moment.

Nervously, I checked my watch every few minutes.

I was once again looking down at my timepiece when suddenly the back door of the warehouse flung open.

'Started the celebrations without us, I see!"

We all erupted into a cheer as Heffinck and his partner came walking in.

I walked over and handed my friend a drink. I had never been so happy to see his balding head before in my life.

The destruction of the factory was a big win for the resistance network. We were elated for sure, but the celebrations were slightly dampened by the events of earlier during the night. We said another toast, drinking to the bravery and patriotism of the two men who had lost their lives during the shoot-out with the German convoy.

Half an hour after Heffinck and his partner arrived, one-by-one we all left the warehouse, disappearing in different directions.

I am proud to report to that we all made it to various shelters and safe houses around town, and that the Germans never managed to arrest anyone involved in the factory explosion.

Once the factory had been blown up, my mission was completed. Several smaller resistance acts took place over the next week, but I didn't play an active role in those. I mostly stayed in the mission headquarters, sending updates to England via wire and celebrating with the men when they returned from successful sabotage operations.

It was too risky for me to venture out much. If the Germans stopped me and if they made the link between me and the factory explosion, it could potentially endanger not just my own life, but that of many of my compatriots.

After tying up a few loose ends, I was ordered to return to England, leaving Belgium in early September.

Unbeknownst to me, I would not return until my home country was no longer at war.

CHAPTER NINE

Return to the UK

W hen I returned to England in September 1944, it quickly became clear that it was unlikely that I would be sent on any further assignments. Paris had been liberated in August, and the Third Reich was now visibly starting to crumble. We couldn't be sure of anything just yet, but optimism was definitely in the air. After five long years of living in fear and uncertainty, people were cautiously beginning to think about their future again.

As soon as I got back, I heard from several friends in the SOE that the agency was slowly starting to dwindle down and that agents were being released from their duties.

After a week of leave, I was summoned to Baker Street. It was a beautiful fall day, so I decided to walk over to the SOE headquarters as opposed to taking the tram.

As I walked the streets of London, I wondered if this was it. If after two-and-a-half years my career as a Special Operations Executive agent was coming to an end.

From the second I set foot in the office, things felt different. The office that was typically a non-stop come and go of people, filled with the sound of typewriter clatter and phones ringing off the hook, now felt eerily quiet.

I checked in at the front desk and took a seat in the waiting area, sitting down in the exact same chair I had sat in the very first time I visited Baker Street with

Andre. I looked down the hallway and thought back at the pointy ladies' shoe I had seen that day. Today the door was closed, and I wondered where that girl was now.

Continuing down my path of nostalgia, I remembered how nervous I had been for that first meeting. Back then, I had no clue what to expect. Everything was so secretive and new.

Although I had put on a brave face, I remember feeling slightly out of place during that first visit.

I had been wearing a cheap suit that I had been given after my release from Miranda. Although it was presentable, I hadn't quite felt myself in it.

Now I felt completely at ease. Wearing a new navy suit with a dark red tie and a matching pocket square, I looked classy as could be. If it wasn't for my young age, I'm sure people would have mistaken me for a director instead of a simple agent. I didn't just feel like I belonged here; I knew I did.

I was proud of everything I had accomplished since that initial meeting. I had pushed myself to my physical limit, enduring months of harsh training. I had faced many fears, jumping out of planes, taking part in secret missions during which many good men paid the ultimate price. I had learned new skills, from radio operations to combat, and I had been placed in countless situations that allowed me to learn more about myself than I ever thought I would.

I was no longer the post-concentration camp traumatized kid who had first walked through these doors. I was a confident young man who had served his country during a time when needed the most.

My supervisor appeared from his office down the hall and asked me to join him. As I entered his office, he warmly shook my hand and offered me a seat.

He sat down, paused for a second and gave me a slight smile.

"I think you know why you're here, Leo," he started. His tone was gentle, as if he wasn't sure how I would take the news he was about to deliver.

"I've heard some rumors," I replied, giving away little of my feelings.

He cleared his throat before continuing.

"Things are starting to slow down and we aren't sending as many agents into the field anymore. As a matter of fact, we don't have any plans for further missions into Belgium. At the end of the month, you will be released back to the Belgian Army. The Special Operations Executive thanks you for your service."

In true British fashion, he had kept it short and formal.

What a gentlemanlike dismissal coming from the ministry of ungentlemanly warfare, I thought as I walked out of the office.

Just like that, I was no longer a spy.

I felt a mix of emotions at that notion. I was smart enough to realize that not every agent is lucky enough to live to see this day, yet it felt sad.

For the past two-and-a-half years, the SOE had been my entire life. There had been ups and downs, but once I was fully committed, I had put everything on the line for the agency. My fellow agents were my brothers, my missions were my sole purpose. The excitement, the thrills, the adrenaline. Now it was all in the past, and I would likely never get to experience those feelings at that same level ever again.

As I walked out into the street, I considered entering the first pub I passed and spending the afternoon alone with my thoughts and a few drinks, but I quickly changed my mind.

If today was the first day of the rest of my life, I knew who I wanted to spend it with.

I strolled over to the guesthouse where Mariette was staying, picked up some flowers on the way, and knocked at her door.

Looking stunning as ever, she was quite surprised to see me show up unannounced in the middle of the day. Of course, I couldn't tell her about what had just happened, but I think she could tell that this hadn't been just an ordinary day for me.

We had been seeing each other regularly over the past two years, but my tendency to disappear for several months on end had made things challenging.

Still, we had grown closer over time and she had confided in me that not long before we met, she had been involved with a British RAF pilot who was shot down over the North Sea. It had taken her a while to get over the loss. Once she had entrusted me with this information though, it was as if the wall around her heart slowly started to crumble. I think she was still scared to lose me, too, but she was cautiously letting me into her heart.

She kissed me and accepted the flowers, but told me she was running late for her shift at the Red Cross.

We agreed to meet up the following day for a game of tennis.

I picked her up the following afternoon and together we rode our bikes to the nearby tennis courts.

I had digested the news from the previous day well and was feeling unusually cheerful. I could tell that Mariette, too, was excited to spend a couple of hours on the tennis court, away from the wartime worries of daily life.

We were having a great time, when suddenly, in the middle of our second set, the unmistakable sound of a V-1 rocket emerged.

We stopped playing, and both looked up at the sky.

"There she is," Mariette said, pointing up into the distance at the flying bomb whizzing through the sky.

Persistent until the very end, the Germans weren't ready to surrender just yet. V-1 and V-2 rockets had been hounding the city for months now. The unmanned rockets would appear out of nowhere, their noise sending Londoners scrambling.

It wasn't until the noise stopped and the bomb started its descent that the panic really started. There was no way of knowing where the bomb would fall and people would run in all directions, sometimes unknowingly running right into the bomb's path.

"Do you want to go in?" I asked, more out of politeness than actual concern.

Mariette looked at me from the other side of the court.

"Keep calm and carry on," she shouted across the net, then threw the tennis ball in the air and hit a great serve straight down the center service line.

Right in that moment, there was no doubt in my mind. This was the girl I was going to marry.

Author's Note

Throughout my childhood, Sunday evening dinner habitually took place at my grandparents' home. Some of my fondest memories of those evenings are the many hours I spent looking through my grandfather's extensive collection of family photographs. An entire glass cupboard was filled with chronologically ordered albums dating back to the 1890s.

Every time I pulled out the 1940-1945 album, I knew I was in for a treat. Each photograph was brought to life by my grandfather's great storytelling skills. At a young age, I was introduced to stories of chucking German's into the docks, avoiding the Foreign Legion by escaping out of bathroom windows, life at Miranda, and much more.

My grandfather passed away when I was fourteen, taking with him his stories and the answers to the many questions I still wanted to ask.

As I was writing this book, I found myself over and over again wishing I could have just one more evening with my grandfather, looking through those books together and listening to his stories. This, of course, was impossible, but ever the record keeper, my grandfather left me with a remarkable amount of documentation that, along with the memory of his stories, formed the base of this book.

The vast majority of this book is based on a true story. Not wanting to overdramatize another person's story, I stuck to the facts as much as possible and tried to only color in scenes for readability purposes.

At the end of the war, my grandfather, Leonard Sonck, proposed to my grandmother, Mariette Loubry. They moved back to Belgium and were married in September 1946. They remained married until my grandfather's death in 2016.

After returning to Antwerp, Leonard worked with his father in the family ship chandler and lumber company. Just as before the war, Leonard didn't stay there very long. After a few years, my grandparents moved to Australia, where Mariette's family, her parents and her brother, had moved to in 1947.

Australia wasn't the right fit for them, and they moved back to Belgium a few years later.

After twelve years of marriage, they welcomed their only daughter, my mother Carine.

Leonard stayed in contact with his friend Henri Heffinck until his death in 1981. Despite his many achievements as a Belgian resistance fighter, Henri preferred not to talk about his wartime actions. After the conclusion of the war, he was awarded numerous military awards by the British, French and Belgian government.

We used to tell my grandfather that his story should be turned into a book. He never knew that his granddaughter would be the one to write it. Now, all I can hope is that my writing did his story justice.

Acknowledgements

There were many times when I didn't think this book would ever be completed. After hours of research, I often felt like I hadn't gotten any further than where I had started.

I often got so caught up in wanting to tell the most accurate version of the truth that I get stuck, and couldn't get another word on paper. Without the encouragement and help of friends and family, I am not sure if this work would have ever developed into a book.

Most importantly, I want to thank my parents for encouraging me throughout the process of writing this book, for critically reading each draft, and for providing me with the most perfect spot to complete my writing and editing process. Having heard my grandfather's stories alongside me, they were often able to provide me with details I was no longer sure of.

I would also like to thank my friends who knew that I was writing this book, for keeping me accountable. There are several people who asked me about the progress on my book every single time I saw them. Thank you for pushing me to keep writing.

Made in the USA
Coppell, TX
20 December 2020